RAGING ON

The "Rage" True Crime Series
Book 2

PAULA MAY

WILDBLUE
PRESS

WildBluePress.com

RAGING ON published by:
WILDBLUE PRESS
P.O. Box 102440
Denver, Colorado 80250

ISBN 978-1-952225-66-6 Trade Paperback
ISBN 978-1-952225-65-9 eBook

Cover design © 2021 WildBlue Press. All rights reserved.

Interior Formatting by Elijah Toten
www.totencreative.com

Book Cover Design by VilaDesign

RAGING ON

ACKNOWLEDGEMENTS

Both this book and its predecessor, *First Degree Rage: The True Story of 'The Assassin,' An Obsession and Murder,* would not be possible but for the input and encouragement of many people to whom I wish to express my sincere appreciation:

To Sheriff James C. "Red" Lyons, whose confidence and trust from the very beginning inspired me to serve God and others to the best of my ability, whose encouragement motivated me to view obstacles only as opportunities, and whose wisdom I have leaned on many times through the years.

To Charlene Norris, my greatest defender, for her loyalty, her ongoing support and encouragement, and her constant availability to me to bounce off ideas, to listen when I need to vent, and to provide sound advice with each new challenge I face.

To Don Gale, for his relentless investigative work, his spirit of teamwork and friendship throughout the years, his willingness to join me in presenting our investigative efforts, and the challenges we faced in public forums to others, and for the time and effort he spent assisting me with this project.

To Terry Agner, for his diligent investigative work, his spirit of teamwork and friendship throughout the years, and for his willingness to assist me with this project.

To Randy Townsend, for his support and patience throughout the investigation, his enduring friendship, and his assistance on these projects.

To Lisa, for her fortitude, candor, and willingness not only to share the pertinent events as she experienced them but also the psychological dynamics accompanying them.

To Tom Rusher, whose diligence and relentless work ethic ultimately kept us all safe.

To Sheriff L. D. Hagaman, for his ongoing support and professionalism.

To Jason Weden, for his willingness to share his trials and his triumphs publicly.

To Kay Weden, for her constant friendship through the years, her mentally and physically exhaustive efforts to assist me with both of these projects, the strength she exhibits daily, her willingness to share her life story including the painful moments as well as the victories, and her ongoing desire to make a positive difference in the lives of others with her story.

To Steve Jackson, Michael Cordova, my editors, and all the staff of WildBlue Press for taking a chance on me as a new writer, and for all the work accomplished on our projects.

To Jeff Hemric, for his abiding love, patience, and encouragement, his sound advice and ever-present mindfulness and application of Christian principles to life's situations, his enduring friendship, companionship, and his assistance with these projects.

To my precious daughter, Caitlin, and her loving husband, Jonathan Fansler, my faithful parents, Gail and Allen Millsaps, my awesome brothers, Roscoe and Josh, my amazing sister, Shannon, and all the rest of my incredible and supportive family, I thank you all from the depths of my heart for your unconditional love, encouragement, and inspiration.

Finally, to my loving, triune Creator God, without whom nothing, including me, would even be possible; I owe my life, my love, and eternal gratitude for a bounty of blessings that, like the apostle John so accurately stated, "If they should be written every one, I suppose that even the world itself could not contain the books that should be written. Amen." (John 21:25)

"Fear is pain arising from the anticipation of evil." - Aristotle

CHAPTER ONE

"There is no fear in love; but perfect love casteth out fear: because fear hath torment."
(I John 4:18)

When someone wants to kill you, somehow you just know it. You carry the knowledge around like a dirty secret that no one else knows. The weight of it is heavy and cold. You feel the chill deep in your bones, in the marrow. You cannot possibly feel safe anywhere, no matter how many people surround you at any given time. You do not feel comfortable sharing this datum with others because they might suppose that it is entirely your fault that another person wants to kill you, that you somehow brought it all upon yourself, and that you are somehow deserving of it. So, you keep it to yourself, hidden inside the recesses of your mind, trying not to allow it to seep out into your daily life. Yet somehow it does.

Random, imaginary scenarios pop into your head at the most inconvenient of times where suddenly he is just *there* – in the same restaurant, the grocery store, at the gas station, in your church, or worse yet inside your child's daycare center, her school, and there is no escape from that evil, hate-filled man. It matters not that such visions are irrational; the fear has a life of its own.

I suppose that a rather naïve part of me surmised that if my intentions were noble and my motives pure, surely no one would *really* wish me dead. I personally would not wish death upon even the worst of my enemies. I vainly hoped that people could see that I basically endeavored to be a good person who genuinely desired to help others, and that at the end of the day, these truths alone would be sufficient enough to counter the malice someone might have towards me. The not-so-naïve part of me, however, knew better. I had, after all, been an officer of the law – specifically, an investigator of violent crime in the most heinous of cases – for far too long to give serious credence to such naïve conjecture. On the contrary, I found myself in the unfortunate locus of the guiles of a dangerous sociopath. I knew it to be true, with every fiber of my being; he wanted me dead, good and dead, and dead for good.

"It's not paranoia when someone really *is* out to get you," my college psychology professor used to point out. How right he was.

I knew in the larger scheme of things that what I feared most was not rational under the current circumstances, yet evil rarely makes sense. I had come to realize that the vast majority of the population is unaware of the sheer magnitude of evil in their quaint little towns, their neighborhoods, and sometimes even in their own trusty circle of family and friends. For better or worse, I was not one of the blessedly oblivious majority.

While the logical portion of my brain declared the prospect of a man intent on killing me to be preposterous, the remainder of my being somehow sensed his evil intentions directed towards me and endeavored to recoil from the possibility as quickly and as far away as possible. This rather intuitive phenomenon had proven to be valid and reliable throughout my law enforcement career, acting as a warning system to alert me when danger was nigh. It served me well, not because of any special gift or talent I possessed, but perhaps because I have witnessed, several times over, the aftermath of pure hatred.

Pure hatred is never just an emotion. It is the cornerstone on which the pillars of malice aforethought, premeditation, and deliberation are built – those elements that legally characterize a homicide as a First-Degree Murder. Pure hatred permeates. It becomes the driving force for unthinkable acts of terror and violence. Hatred is palpable, and to me, familiar. Having encountered it many times over in my career, it was now even more terrible, in a personal way, as it was suddenly directed *towards* me. Its effect was a fear I could not shake, a fear that would rear its ugly head without warning. It was the kind of fear that can become debilitating if not kept in check.

Such a fear manifests itself in a variety of ways, and its effects are pervasive. At times, for instance, in the middle of an otherwise ordinary day, something suddenly appears out of the blue as a reminder that you are not truly safe because there is another person perfectly proficient in the business of murder who wants you dead…not merely dead, really, but brutally killed. You feel as if you cannot draw a full breath because the fear weighs so heavily upon your chest.

Some nights, you wake suddenly in the darkest hour of night to find your muscles tense and your hands drawn tightly into fists, following a nightmare in which a convicted murderer with a single purpose of mind walks out of a prison unrestrained. Then there are other nights in which your eyes fly open, and you are instantly awake with heart racing when a tree limb outside your bedroom window cracks or brushes up against the house. You imagine someone is there, and you imagine his face pressed against the glass of your windowpane. You imagine *his* face specifically because it is as nearly as familiar as your own.

The knowledge that the man, who hates you with so much undisguised contempt, is incarcerated at that point in time is of limited comfort because you know well that violent prison inmates are released for one reason or another every single day. Some escape on their own. Some merely employ another to carry out their evil devices. Having worked in the criminal justice system – and specifically in the profession of law enforcement – for more than a decade was more than a sufficient amount of time to see violent offenders incarcerated, released, incarcerated, and released, again and again. Recidivism is a harsh reality in today's society.

All things considered, it is practically impossible to hide from a man who harbors such depths of hatred, even a man who is confined to a 6 x 9 x 12-foot dwelling. A man thus possessed will not be easily thwarted. His hatred will be neither forgotten nor abandoned. Time itself only seems to fuel its flames, particularly time spent in the state penitentiary where there is little else but self-pity and vengeance to occupy a man's thoughts, and where his imagination grows wild and unchecked.

L. C. Underwood had nothing *but* time: a "life" sentence equating to approximately twenty years in prison for First Degree Murder, plus forty years on top of that (consecutively and not concurrently) for First Degree Kidnapping. As it happened, I was the chief investigator in the homicide case of which he was convicted, and the latest object of Underwood's incessant and interminable hatred. As such, I was all too familiar with L. C. Underwood's grisly and gruesome capabilities. He perceived me, and not his own willful and deliberate actions, to be the chief reason for his current plight. The fact that I was a woman only exacerbated his hatred towards me, for reasons I had only just begun to comprehend in the summer of 1997.

Over the years, I had learned a great deal about the seemingly boundless capability of one person to enact atrocities upon another, not nearly as much from my criminology degrees as from the experience I had acquired throughout my career as a criminal detective, having investigated a number of crimes against persons such as stalking, communicated threats, domestic abuse, rapes, and other sexual assaults, and many other cases from minor to extreme violence. I was familiar with misogyny, that (generally subconscious) hatred that misogynistic men developed early in life. I understood that it typically occurred as a result of some type of betrayal or traumatic experience that had, more often than not, involved a maternal figure in whom they had trusted. Whatever the cause, misogynists were particularly frightening to me because it seemed that both their anger and propensity for violence was limitless. They were also not above employing another to carry out their evil devices if necessary, as L. C. Underwood had already proven.

I thought of the countless hours that went by as I was challenged, verbally attacked, and interrogated on the witness stand, testifying against him in his jury trial, State of North Carolina vs. Lamont Claxton "L.C." Underwood; a homicide trial that took nearly four weeks to complete. I sensed his cold, penetrating eyes on me as I directed my answers towards the jury. I could only guess at the atrocities he imagined against me, and not only due to my courtroom testimony. I was not the only person on his hate list, but I was definitely in the top three.

Over time, I had risen to the top of his growing list of intended targets, having singlehandedly provoked his wrath much earlier, when I objected to a bond reduction requested by his attorneys shortly after his arrest, and months before that, when I obtained search warrants for his home; searches which resulted in the discovery of physical evidence which ultimately led to his conviction. My strategically constructed statements to the news media, witnesses, and others throughout the investigation further infuriated L. C. Underwood, a markedly narcissistic man who thought himself far too clever to be caught for any of his evil deeds. His efforts to manipulate me psychologically while he was in custody in a jail cell just down the hall from my office had failed miserably. His hatred for me was demonstrated in every spiteful word he spoke of me or wrote in his own hand, and in the rudimentary and most unflattering pictures he drew of me in vivid crayon color while he awaited trial for First Degree Murder. I prayed that God would thwart every effort he made towards getting out of prison, for all our sakes.

Ironically, L. C. Underwood was a fellow law enforcement officer who had worked in the same geographical region of North Carolina as I for several years, yet I had never met nor even so much as heard the man's name. Our commonly shared means of earning a living was where our similarities both commenced and concluded, and I was more than a little glad for that. Our paths, however, were fated to cross when he inadvertently and unwillingly invited me into his life in December of 1993, and he would impact my own life in unwelcome ways for many years to come.

CHAPTER TWO

**"For God hath not given us the spirit of
fear; but of power, and of love,
and of a sound mind." (2 Timothy 1:7)**

The clear sky and gentle breeze gave no hint of what was to come. Although the afternoon temperature had risen above 50 degrees, sundown left a frigid chill in the atmosphere. At 9:00 PM, it was barely above freezing at 33 degrees Fahrenheit in Salisbury, North Carolina, a town of about 32,000 people. Salisbury was the county seat of Rowan County and located to the southeast of my hometown of Boone where I was born, attended school, completed two college degrees, and was currently working as a Detective with the Watauga County Sheriff's Office. I was energetic and industrious, and at the time I was investigating yet another domestic violence-related homicide, unaware of the events that were taking place at that time in the City of Salisbury. Not many days hence, however, I would absorb every last detail.

It was the night of Friday, December 3, 1993, and as had fast become his habit, L. C. Underwood was driving in the night for the sole purpose of stalking his ex-fiancé, unbeknownst to her. Kay Weden, an attractive, middle-aged, high school English teacher, single mom to a teenage son, was more than a little relieved to be out of the long-term, dysfunctional relationship in which she had been entangled with him. She felt sorry for him, in a way, as many women would for such a man, what with his deep-seated insecurities and the unexpected fear of abandonment he possessed, but now she decidedly wanted nothing more to do with him and had told him just that on several occasions. He was forty-two years old and certainly capable of living without her. Being the compassionate person that she was, Kay hoped that L. C. would truly find happiness with someone else, even though she doubted whether he ever could. In any case, he was no longer her problem, or so she believed.

Kay was determined to look towards the future. For the first time in a long time, Kay was happy to be in a newly developing and promising relationship with the much kinder, gentler, and even more handsome man, Viktor Gunnarsson. Viktor was, in fact, visiting Kay at her residence in Salisbury, North Carolina on that fateful night, following a pleasant dinner at a nearby seafood restaurant where Kay had introduced Viktor to her elderly, widowed mother, Catherine Miller.

Neither Kay nor Viktor had any idea that, as they chatted peacefully around her firepit beside her modest brick ranch home, L. C. Underwood's stalking efforts had resulted in his spotting the unfamiliar car in Kay's driveway and had rushed home to make a phone call. He caught himself before he dialed central dispatch to run a 10-28, a check on the license plate information.

L. C. was on suspension for an ugly little scene he caused involving Kay at a Salisbury restaurant. Thus, he was not supposed to be working in law enforcement in any capacity, so he decided instead to call a buddy and ask him to run the license plate check for him. Rick Hillard had been a deputy with the Rowan County Sheriff's Department for the past several years. He had also been a faithful friend to L. C.; even going out with him on weekends mostly because he felt sorry for him. But before they could go to dinner or the clubs or do anything else, L. C. always had to "check up on Kay." Rick was becoming a bit concerned about L. C.'s relationship with Kay, which seemed like more of a one-sided obsession to Rick than a mutual, romantic relationship.

In fact, Rick had only recently learned that his brother, Danny, who had been hanging out with L. C. more recently, had gone with L. C. to Bogart's Restaurant in Salisbury where L. C. had confronted Kay having dinner with another man, and where L. C. had dumped a glass of tea into Kay's lap after losing his cool. The restaurant manager called the police, and L. C. found himself to be the latest subject of an internal affairs investigation.

"Danny, maybe you should stop running around with L. C.; at least till he gets Kay Weden out of his head," Rick cautioned his brother when he dropped by.

"I know. When it comes to Kay, he does something stupid."

"Well, that last little stunt he pulled at Bogart's has gotten him fired," Rick informed Danny.

"Yeah, I heard," Danny said. "I told him before he ever walked over to their table it was a bad idea."

"He should've listened."

"Well, if common sense was lard, L. C. wouldn't have enough to grease a pan."

"Hopefully, he learned his lesson," Rick said.

Rick, however, was not thinking about L. C.'s obsession with Kay Weden when he answered his phone call on the night of Friday, December 3rd. He was just about to go to bed when L. C. called, asking for a minor favor that wouldn't take but a few minutes of his time. Rick agreed to help L. C. who was, after all, a fairly convincing liar.

L. C. thought that he had better make up some kind of story to tell his friend if he was going to have Rick run the plate, so he told Rick that a suspicious car had just backed all the way up his driveway, stopped momentarily, and then drove back down the street. L. C. said that he saw the car from inside his house and had stepped outside to see who it was, and that was when L. C. was able to get the license plate number. It seemed odd to Rick that someone would *back* up L. C.'s driveway, which was on somewhat of an incline, rather than pull straight in from the street, but Rick did not dwell on it as he called the Rowan County Communication Center to run the vehicle tag for his friend.

A few minutes later, Rick called L. C. back at home and provided him with the information he sought. The license plate was valid; it came back to a white male by the name of Viktor Ake Lennart Gunnarsson, age 40. L. C. learned that Viktor Gunnarsson resided at 910 Lakewood Apartments in Salisbury. Lakewood Apartments was only about a ten-minute drive from L. C.'s home on Lake Drive in Salisbury. Several weeks would pass before Rick Hillard would be raking his hands through his short, dark hair, repeatedly regretting having broken what seemed to be a minor administrative regulation in order to perform a small favor for a friend and fellow officer. Rick blamed himself for obtaining the information for L. C., but L. C. had lied to him about where he obtained the vehicle's license plate number in the first place.

It was the last night Viktor Gunnarsson was known to be alive. Kay recalled Viktor's goodnight kiss as one of passion and promise. The two new lovers had made plans to spend more time together on the following day, but the midnight hour was approaching, and it had been a long day for both of them. Viktor left Kay's house, stopped at a convenience store along the way where he purchased a gallon of milk, and then drove the remaining distance to his apartment complex. After parking his older model Lincoln in his usual space in front of his apartment building, Viktor walked up the single flight of exterior steps, turned, and walked only a few steps more to the front door of his end unit. He unlocked his apartment door and went inside to retire for the evening. He needed to get some sleep if he was going to tutor his language students in the morning and then spend the afternoon and evening with Kay.

Meanwhile, seething with rage he was barely able to contain, Salisbury Police Officer Lamont Claxton "L. C." Underwood left his own residence on Lake Drive in Salisbury at approximately midnight in his spotless burgundy Chevrolet Monte Carlo. He drove to Lakewood Apartments where he easily located Viktor Gunnarsson's second story end unit #910. Viktor had not been home long, but as I would see for myself inside Viktor's apartment not many days hence, Viktor had gotten into bed and had probably even fallen asleep when L. C. Underwood showed up, undoubtedly flashing his police badge.

Shortly thereafter, Viktor Gunnarsson found himself bound and gagged in the trunk of the Monte Carlo of a man he had never met nor even heard of; a man claiming to be a police officer, but who clearly had anything but lawful intentions towards him. Viktor Gunnarsson was not unfamiliar with the police, as he had been arrested less than a decade earlier in his home country of Sweden, where he was charged with the assassination of Prime Minister Olof Palme. Released a few days later as a result of a lack of evidence, he fled to the United States seeking political asylum, following a flood of media attention to which he, his hardworking parents and siblings, were unaccustomed and unprepared. It was through a mutual friend in North Carolina by the name of Tana that the easygoing and charming Viktor Gunnarsson had met Kay Weden.

For the next two hours following his initial abduction, Viktor Gunnarsson struggled unsuccessfully to escape both his conveyance and his bindings, as the outside temperature dropped considerably below the freezing point on the ride northwest to the Appalachian Mountains, to the outskirts of Boone, North Carolina. They arrived at a rural community known as Deep Gap, well within my law enforcement jurisdiction with the county sheriff's office. But it would take more than a month for Viktor Gunnarsson's nude and frozen body to be found.

The decedent was discovered at the base of a fallen tree in a wooded area on January 7, 1994 under a blanket of snow, with two fatal gunshot wounds. Just like that, Viktor Gunnarsson's exciting life had come to an end far, far away from his beloved homeland and family.

Meanwhile, on December 4th and 5th, Kay Weden waited in vain for Viktor to call her again. She and her friend Tana, giddy as schoolgirls, drove through Viktor's apartment complex in an effort to gain some possible insight as to what might be keeping Viktor away. Once in the parking lot, Kay and Tana found Viktor's older model Lincoln in its usual parking space, and the door to Viktor's apartment door slightly ajar. They knocked, but receiving no answer, they dared to peek inside, finding the apartment warm but empty. As time passed with no word from Viktor, Kay eventually reached the conclusion that he was no longer interested in her, surprising herself with the realization of how much she had grown to care about Viktor Gunnarsson in such a short period of time.

In the days that followed, Kay found herself confused, thinking frequently of Viktor and how they had both seemed to enjoy the time they had spent together. She did not understand why he would not even return her calls. They had had such a pleasant evening together on the past Friday, their last evening together, that it simply made no sense. Could it have been so long since she was in a normal dating relationship that she had totally misread Viktor's intentions towards her? Tana was also somewhat baffled; she had been convinced by her own observations that Viktor and Kay had a good thing going on.

In the early afternoon hours of Sunday, the fifth of December, Kay's phone rang multiple times, and each time it did, she optimistically rushed to answer it, but it was never Viktor who was calling. It was L. C. demanding to see her. She could not have been more annoyed.

"What is it you want, L.C.?" Kay asked impatiently.

"Kay, Honey, I'm coming over there to pick you up, and we're going to get this relationship back on track," he announced firmly, "the way it's supposed to be."

"What? No, L. C. Just… no." What was he thinking? They were broken up, and she had no intentions of ever getting back together with him.

"Why not, Kay?" L. C.'s voice was tense. She could tell he was already angry with her. She wondered vaguely if he had been drinking, although he rarely drank enough alcohol to lose control.

"I've already explained all that to you, L. C.," Kay said, exasperated.

L. C. did not appreciate her tone. Angrily, he said, "…I know you're seeing other men…like the man you had your mother meet at Blue Bay Seafood." There. He had given himself away already, but Kay did not pause to wonder how L. C. knew that she had had dinner with Viktor and her mother on Friday night before Viktor came to her house.

"Oh, that's Tana's friend," Kay found herself explaining. Then she wondered why she was bothering to explain because she owed L. C. nothing, not even the courtesy of taking his calls. She had asked him to stop contacting her, but L. C. was not a man who easily took no for an answer.

"How did your mother like your new boyfriend?" L. C. asked, unable to disguise his blatant sarcasm.

"Um, she liked him okay," Kay responded. It was then that she began to wonder how L. C. could possibly know that she had gone to dinner on Friday with her mother and Viktor. *Could L. C. be following her?*

"I'll bet she did …especially since your mother hates *me,"* L. C. retorted.

Kay sighed. This was not a new topic of conversation with L. C. Underwood. He had made up his mind that Catherine Miller despised him. Truth be told, it was he who despised *her*. It was not fair that Kay should have a devoted, loving mother to dote on her when his own mother had basically thrown him away as a small child. He hated his own mother, and, at best, he resented Kay's. It made perfect sense in a psychology textbook kind of way, but it made no sense to Kay, who had been witness to the many acts of kindness that Catherine had bestowed upon L. C., even though Catherine had discreetly advised Kay to stay away from him.

L. C. was still whining on the phone about Kay's mother. "L. C., I have told you before; my mother does note hate *anybody*. And if you've really changed like told me you have, then you should just talk to her. Tell her how you feel. I'm sure she'll understand."

L. C. was quiet for a moment. Then he asked, "Do you really think so? Do you think I should go talk to her?"

Kay glanced at the clock on the wall. *Why hadn't Viktor called?*

She was only halfheartedly listening to L. C. She said into the phone, "That's up to you, L. C. But listen… You have to stop trying to make decisions for me." Kay did not want L. C. trying to intimidate her into declining dinner with Viktor and her mother again if she so decided. If she got another opportunity, she definitely wanted to see Viktor again.

"I am not trying to make decisions for you!" His anger returned.

"Yes, you are!" she replied.

"How?" he asked, as if he really did not know.

"Well, for one thing, you can't just announce that you are coming over here and demand that I go out with you!"

"But…"

"See! You have to stop trying to make decisions for me!"

"I'm not."

"Yes, you are."

"I am not!"

Kay glanced up at Tana who was staring at Kay on the phone and shaking her head in disbelief.

"L. C., I have to go now," Kay announced.

"Why? Is someone there?" he asked.

"Yes, a friend of mine is here. A *woman* friend."

"I thought you said you had things to do," L. C. said accusingly.

"She's helping me."

"Right," L. C. said and slammed the phone down hard.

Kay was embarrassed, and her friend Tana was embarrassed for her, and more than a little concerned about L. C. Underwood. But soon Kay and Tana were relaxing and enjoying the evening, chatting like high school girlfriends at a pajama party and occasionally coming up with a plethora of plausible possibilities as to why Viktor had not yet gotten in touch with Kay.

L. C. called again the following day, Monday, the sixth of December. This time when he called, Kay's friend, Vicky, was there. Kay told L. C. that she could not talk to him because she and Vicky were about to leave.

"You're going out?" L. C. asked, as innocently as he could muster.

"I'm going to Spencer's tonight with some of my *girl*friends to celebrate my friend Anne's birthday. But I have to run some errands first, like pick up her gift, and I'm running out of time. Plus, I have to stop by and pick up my mother too, so I have to go now." Kay put down the phone. How dare she blow him off like that, L. C. would later complain.

Vicky, Kay, and Catherine Miller arrived at Spencer's Restaurant in Salisbury at 7:00. They were seated inside, enjoying dinner with their friends, when L. C. walked in with a pretty woman on his arm. Kay had no idea that L. C. had quickly and secretly bribed his "date" to pretend to be a fictitious woman named "Kim" and to accompany him to Spencer's Restaurant where he could flaunt her in front of Kay.

Angry with herself that she had told L. C. where she was going and that L. C. had obviously followed her there, bringing with him a pretty woman Kay had never seen before, Kay walked out. L. C. was pleased to see that he obviously had the power to get to her. He told his "date," who was actually a friend of a friend that needed some money and had been hired to go to dinner with L. C. and openly flirt with him in plain view of his ex-fiancé, that things had gone even better than he had hoped. Her name was Wanda, and she would prove to be a valuable and cooperative witness in court.

Later that night at home, Kay was frustrated through and through that L. C. had ruined yet another evening for her. She was frustrated with him and also with herself for letting him get to her. She really did not care who L. C. dated. But knowing that he had just shown up with a date where she and her friends were supposed to be celebrating infuriated Kay. He was already on suspension for the incident at Bogart's Restaurant, but not even his suspension from the Salisbury Police Department had stopped him from showing up in a restaurant again tonight where Kay was simply trying to enjoy a meal.

Truth be told, she was equally frustrated with Viktor for not having returned any of her calls. She had tried to call him, had left multiple messages on his answering machine, but she had heard neither hide nor hair from him. But tomorrow was another day. In fact, it was to be a special day for her son, Jason, her only child who was about to turn sixteen, and she vowed to enjoy the day with him; the day he would get his driver's license. Jason was a good boy, a fine student, a strong, successful athlete, and the greatest blessing of her life. She had taken the day off from work to spend Jason's birthday with him. Kay went to bed early, but had trouble falling asleep. When at last she did, she slept fitfully.

At 6:45 AM on Tuesday, December 7th, Kay woke to the ringing of her phone. Half asleep, she let the answering machine pick up, and then she heard L. C.'s voice. "Kay, I put a letter for you in your mailbox. I, I hope you'll read it…" Her mind began to reel; there was no going back to sleep. Curiosity getting the better of her, Kay got out of bed, put on her robe and slippers, and walked outside. She opened the mailbox and found L. C.'s letter. She carried it back inside without opening the envelope. She needed some caffeine.

Before she could get a pot of coffee on, however, her doorbell rang. She walked to the door and opened it partway.

"L. C.," she said, not entirely surprised.

"Kay, I'd really like to talk to you for a minute," he said, somewhat out of breath.

Too groggy to argue, she opened the door all the way and said, "Come in." Jason, who normally would have already left for school, was still asleep in his room.

L. C. followed her into the living area, and they sat down. He got right to the point.

"I want to talk about us, about our relationship, Kay." He was exasperating.

"L. C., I've *told* you. I'm not interested in a relationship right now."

"You told me you loved me," he countered. How she wished she had never said those three words to him.

"L. C., I'm not *in love* with you… You push too hard. You can't seem to just ease up and …just let things be normal. I care about you, but I need my freedom and my space. I don't want to be accountable to anyone, including you. I'm sorry, but I don't." It was the same conversation they had several times over.

At various points during this conversation, L. C. got out of his chair and walked towards her. Kay told him more than once to sit back down and just listen. Kay could see L. C. was struggling to stay calm.

Kay walked into the kitchen to fill her coffee cup, and L. C. followed her. She hoped he would leave soon. Then L. C. told her something awful.

"Misty died," he announced flatly. Misty was L. C.'s Shetland Sheepdog. Kay knew he loved Misty. She had bought the dog for L. C. as a Christmas gift the year before, and she loved Misty too. L. C. told her the dog choked on a quarter. Later, he told a fellow police officer the dog electrocuted herself. He told yet another story to someone else about how the dog died. No one ever found out what really happened to the dog, and in fact, no one ever found the dog's carcass. At least two witnesses had seen L. C. kick the dog for no good reason when they had visited on occasion inside L. C.'s house. L. C. had a history of abusing animals as far back as his stay at the orphanage where he grew up, but Kay had no way of knowing such a thing or she would never have given him the dog as a gift.

"Oh no, L. C. I am so sorry!" Kay was genuinely upset.

"Thanks," L. C. mumbled, not meeting her eyes.

"You must feel just awful," Kay said, though oddly enough, he didn't seem sad at all about Misty.

Kay and L. C. sat at the table in her kitchen, and L. C. quickly changed the subject. "Well, did you read the letter I wrote you?"

Kay exhaled. "I haven't had a chance to, L. C. I just walked to the mailbox and got it." The letter was still lying in a sealed white envelope on the stove. L. C. was staring at it.

Kay tried to make herself clear for the umpteenth time. "I don't want a relationship, L. C. Not with you or with anyone."

L. C. looked at her, pushed back his chair, walked to the door, and as he reached for the knob he said, "You don't need to say any more." But he did not touch the envelope.

She should have left well enough alone, but she wanted to make him understand once and for all.

"I care about you as a person, L. C. I'm just not interested in a romantic relationship with you." Why she felt she had to let him down easy after all the misery he had caused her, she could not explain.

L. C.'s eyes hardened for a moment, turning very dark. Then he looked around and asked, "Where's Jason?"

"He's here, in bed asleep. Why?"

L. C. did not answer her. He started to stay something else but then just looked at her blankly for a few moments, stood up, turned around, and left. She felt a chill of a sudden and tightened her robe around her body.

Several hours later Kay found herself staring at the plain white envelope with L. C.'s return address on a sticker in the upper left corner. She finally opened the envelope and took out the five-page hand-written letter with little sympathy and growing agitation as she began to read. It was like so many others he had written her before when she tried to end their relationship.

Kay,

It is Tuesday at 12:10 a.m. and I am at home, Alone. Yes, Kay, Alone, because I love you. I wish you would open your eyes and see that. There are some things I want to say to you. And all that I ask after you read this letter is talk with me on the telephone or in person. I want it to be face to face. I will not mail this letter, because I intend to bring it to your house later today.

First, I want to say that if I had seen your car at Spencer's, I would never have come in. The entire time I was there I wanted to come up to you and tell you that I LOVE YOU. Kay, I know that you have went out with other men since we have been apart, and if that is what you wanted to do, then its O.K. because I couldn't do anything to stop it. It's not that people don't know us in this town and yes people I know have seen you out with other men and couldn't wait to run back to tell me. I am not stupid to think you have been at home all alone. I don't care to know their names and I don't want to know who they were. But let's be honest with each other. I didn't want to go out to eat tonight. But if you knew how each night I eat alone and I get so tired of that I could scream.

I have tried now for almost two months to try to make you understand and something you refuse to do that I had some problems in my life that I had to deal with and yes, I had to get help but I'm facing it head-on. I am the same person you first met. But you refuse to see it. I know you don't want me leaning on you, and I don't want to nor do I intend to. I have tried so long and hard to set things right that I have done wrong. I don't think you understand so I'm saying this all for the final time. Kay Weden, I love you and I want you to love me. My heart is yours and it doesn't belong to anyone else. I want to make a life with you, and I told Kim that, and she understands that.

Last night at Spencer's I told her the entire time we were eating that I wanted so much to get up and come over to you and say in front of everyone at your table, Kay I love you and only you, and take you home with me, and hold you all night. Kim looked at me and she looked over at you and then she said "You both love each other, and I can tell you both want your arms around each other, so don't be stupid. You both are so much in love that being apart makes both of you miserable, so why don't both of you give up some of your pride and make this thing work. She understands that I don't love her, and she knows how I feel about you, and she is not stupid, to know that I have no intentions of loving her, no matter how she feels about me. I don't want a life with her.

Kay, what do I have to do to make you understand my love is yours and yours alone. But darling, you can't expect me to wait forever, and I can only hold in place for so long. I try each day to have the faith to hold on, but I just can't hold on forever. Each day that passes without you my heart breaks a little more. I have tried to talk with you several times but each time you either have company or you can't talk, or you have to go somewhere, or you say I'll call you back, but you never do. I have waited by this phone long enough and I *can't, and I won't anymore. I want to make things right with you and make you see I want you, your love your life to be a part of mine, but you never want to give me that choice, and if that is what you want, say so, and I will get on with my life. <u>I don't want to live my life without you,</u> but if I have to I will. I can't carry this pain and hurt around with me forever.*

It's not fair to me, and I wouldn't do that to you if it were the other way around. Kay you say don't force you into something you don't want to do, well don't force me into something I don't want. I want you, your love, and a life of sharing something that we use to talk about so often. <u>I don't want anyone, but you</u> and I have tried everything I know to show you that. But I don't know what else to do. I have tried getting you to talk with me, but you are always busy.

You told me recently that you didn't want a relationship and if that is what you want, I will let go. I have no other choice. I can only keep trying to come back for so long. My life is getting back to normal, and I want you in it, not as someone who is better than you but as a person that is an equal partner.

I want you to understand what I am about to say. <u>I love you very much</u>. I want you and only you and no one else. I want to talk with you and say I love you to your face. I want to hold you in my arms and kiss you and make love to you. I want to put this relationship back on track and to show <u>you I care for you, and only you. I have not nor do I intend to make love or hold anyone else, until I can't hold you anymore</u>.

I do not want to force you to do something you don't want to do, but don't force me into something I don't want. I do not intend to be mean by saying these things. My days of being mean and cruel are over forever. I have a heart and soul and I am a decent person even if you don't believe that I know it's true. I've made mistakes in life and I am sure I'll make some more mistakes in the future, But not the cruel kind. I do not want to go through the rest of my life without you, a person I do love, and care for with all my heart. But I will not chase you anymore. I've paid the price for my mistakes, but I will not pay for them for the rest of my life. No one should have to do that, not me, not you, not anyone. I've told you several times that I would try to spend the rest of my life trying to make up to you for my past mistakes. I love you Kay Weden, and my heart is yours if you want it. I don't want anyone else, but I will not allow my heart to hurt anymore, I have to start healing because my health is important. I've lost so much weight my clothes no longer fit. I have worried, hurt, and lost enough sleep over this. I have asked you to forgive and try to forget the things I have done to hurt you. I've told you that for the things you have said and done to me I don't need to forgive you, because love is never having to say I'm sorry or I forgive you.

Again, I don't want to force you into something you don't want, and I didn't say what I did on the phone to make you mad. I ask you but I will not beg for your love anymore. If this relationship ends, it ends now. And if that is what you want then I'll respect that. But if it does end, I'll leave knowing I tried to make you understand that this man loves you very much and I wanted to make it work. But I have to put my life back together, for my own health and peace of mind, please understand that. I will ask you once more to take the time if this relationship means everything to you to call me today and talk with me or come to my house tonight even after you get through with your Ace program. I would like for you to invite me to go. Kay please don't throw our love away because of pride, and what has happened in the past, and look only to the future. I am willing to meet you more than halfway. If I don't hear from you tonight, I will take it that it's over and I will get on with my life without you. It's not what I want but I can't go on any longer like this. Please don't throw this away. I can do no more than what I've already tried. If you decide not to call or come back to try to make this work. I wish you all the best of what life has to offer. I want to go away with you for the weekend if you will go. But if I never hear from you again, I will never say to anyone, no matter what it has cost me that I regret having met you, but most of all, falling in love with you.

Love, L. C.

It was, in fact, a broken record. The majority of L. C.'s letters were pleas for "just one more chance" and contained some sort of professions of love, but there were also more ominous letters in which he could not hide his smoldering resentment and anger at his loss of control over her life. The emotional roller coaster he kept her on for so many months was exhausting. It had sucked the life out of her, and she wanted no part of being in a personal relationship with L. C. Underwood ever again. For the time being, all she wanted was to celebrate her son's birthday in peace.

Kay took Jason to get his driver's license as planned, after a short visit from her mother, Catherine Miller, who dropped by to wish Jason a happy birthday.

"Is something bothering you, dear?" her mother asked.

"Oh, L. C. was here," Kay responded, sounding exasperated. She told her mother about the letter and her brief discussion with L. C.

Catherine frowned and shook her head. She had done her best to discourage Kay from being involved with L. C. She knew he was no good for her daughter. For that matter, she did not see how he could be any good for anyone. Something was not right about the man; he was not the person he presented himself to be. Something hateful, some type of ill will, some spiteful anger emanated from his person, hidden just beneath the surface but plainly evident to an astute and wise woman like Catherine Miller, a twice-widowed, kind, hardworking and generous pillar of her community on which many had come to rely upon through the years for counsel and encouragement.

Catherine wondered at the possibility that L. C. had something to do with the terrible things Kay had experienced over the past ten or so months. The worst of it had occurred in the spring, just about the time Kay first tried to break up with him.

On March 15, 1993, at 7:15 in the morning, Kay found that her Honda had been spray-painted with red graffiti. Later that same day, she discovered that the garage door at her house had vulgarities spray-painted on the front for all of her neighbors to see.

On March 18th, Kay received a letter through the mail informing her that something bad was going to happen to her son Jason. L. C. told her that he had received an anonymous telephone call threatening Jason's life.

On March 19th, L. C. informed Kay that he had received an anonymous letter at his school resource office at Salisbury High School that stated much of the same, and in addition,

L. C. told her that his house had been "egged."

On March 20th between 2:00 and 4:00 in the morning, someone fired a .22 gunshot into Jason's bedroom of Kay's house while Jason was asleep in bed.

On March 22nd, someone "keyed" Kay's recently repaired Honda car as it sat parked in her driveway.

On March 24th, Kay received another letter in the mail stating that "they" had egged her house, shot at it, and may soon set her house on fire.

Also, during the spring of 1993, Kay received a number of anonymous phone calls from a male caller whose voice she did not recognize. The caller informed her that her son owed money for drugs.

On April 2nd, Jason received an anonymous call on his private bedroom line. The caller threatened to break his legs and ruin his soccer career if he did not pay money owed for drug debt.

On April 3rd, L. C. told Kay that eggs had been thrown at his house and that someone had fired shots into his house.

On April 4th, an unknown man called Kay and stated that if he did not receive his money that the shots that were fired into L. C.'s house would not be warning shots "next time."

On April 5th, an officer brought Kay an anonymous letter at work that he had received in the mail that day. The letter stated that Jason would be hurt badly, and the house would be damaged as well. Kay was more frightened and more frustrated with each passing day.

The anonymous, threatening calls continued, and each time Kay turned to L. C. for comfort and to help her get answers. Jason, to anyone's knowledge who was questioned, did not use drugs, nor did he owe any type of debt to anyone.

While Catherine loved her grandson unconditionally, she was not naïve. Yet, no matter how she looked for any signs whatsoever that Jason was using drugs, she found absolutely nothing in Jason's behavior; his success in school, his friends, absolutely nothing that indicated to her in any way that Jason might somehow be using or dealing illegal drugs or that he owed money to anyone. Jason was a starter on the high school soccer team, and his friends were health-conscious athletes as well who also maintained good grades. But someone, somewhere was trying to make it look like Jason had gotten himself into big trouble and that he was physically in danger. Catherine could not help but worry that Jason *was* in danger – not by some unknown drug dealers but by someone close to Kay and Jason; someone who knew when they came and went, and someone who could pull off terrible things and get away with it.

Could someone be setting up a fictitious scenario that would explain away a planned attack on Jason, or something exponentially worse, such as his disappearance, or murder? Catherine worried more than she ever let on to her only daughter. Kay was upset enough already. In the spring, when the threats were coming so frequently, the police seemed to be zeroing in on L. C. as a suspect. As a police officer, L. C. let Kay know, in no uncertain terms, that his job was on the line at just the mere suggestion that he might be the person behind the anonymous threatening phone calls and letters. L. C. pressured Kay relentlessly with guilt that allowing the police to investigate L. C. would cause him to lose his entire law enforcement career. Eventually, L. C. persuaded Kay to demand that the investigation be stopped. Catherine had even gone with Kay to ask the Police Chief to stop the investigation, but Catherine could not dismiss the possibility that L. C. Underwood was responsible. It was as if L. C. did not want the police to solve the cases Kay reported. Catherine Miller was only trying to support her daughter as best she could, but she certainly did not feel good about it.

Catherine could only hope that the threats, which had seemingly stopped for the time being, would stop for good. Kay and Jason both had suffered unnecessarily since, coincidentally, L. C. Underwood had come into their lives. But Kay simply could not believe that L. C. would terrorize her so. She had been good to L. C., and for that matter, so had Catherine. L. C. was, after all, a public servant sworn to protect and serve others. Catherine, on the other hand, was not so easily swayed by L. C.'s charm.

Kay returned to work on the following morning, Wednesday, December 8th. After having taken the previous day off work to spend with Jason, her busy workday at West Rowan High School passed quickly. When she returned home in the afternoon, she found two hang-up calls on her answering machine, both from L. C.'s home phone, despite her having placed a call block against his home number. How was he able to get around the phone block? And why, for that matter, was he calling her during the day when he knew she would be teaching? Frustrated, she dialed his number, and L. C. answered.

"Did you call me today?" Kay asked.

"Um, I called earlier." L. C. sounded like he had been asleep.

"But why? It's only 3:15 right now. You knew I was working at school earlier in the day."

L. C. never answered her question. "I've been asleep," he said. He clearly was not going to admit the truth or offer any kind of explanation. This was not new behavior. He often did things that made no sense to Kay, and sometimes it seemed he did them just to confuse her. She was more than tired of his erratic behavior.

"So, what time will Jason be home?" L. C. asked her.

"Why do you ask?" she retorted.

"What's the big deal? I just wondered."

"I gotta go, L. C." Jason was none of his business, and it was odd that he was asking about his whereabouts again.

About 5:30 PM, L. C. called again. Kay was straightening up her rec-room. L. C. was in a worse mood than before.

He said with voice audibly trembling, "Kay, you are forcing me to make a life with Kim!"

"I'm not forcing you to do anything, L. C.," Kay said, matter-of-factly. In fact, Kay was hopeful that L. C. *would* become involved with someone else so that he would leave her alone.

"In a sense you are forcing me… I don't want that girl; I want you. But I'm just going to have to go on."

"Do it then," Kay told him and hung up. *Please,* she thought, *Please do it.*

L. C. continued to call, but Kay refused to answer. L. C., however, was relentless. Her phone would not stop ringing. She had already given up on the possibility that one of the many phone calls she was receiving was from Viktor Gunnarsson.

Finally, she answered the phone, knowing that she would have no peace until she did.

"What are you doing?" L. C. asked Kay.

"Watching TV," she answered impatiently.

"Whatcha watching?" he asked nonchalantly.

Kay glanced over at her television which she had been having trouble concentrating on for the ringing phone. "I'm watching *Unsolved Mysteries* on the Lifetime channel," she told him tiredly.

"Oh yeah?" he asked. "What's it about tonight?"

"I don't know yet. It is just coming on." It was a small detail that L. C. would later attempt to use as an alibi for himself when he told investigators that he was home watching TV when, in fact, he was not.

"Oh. So, you're planning on staying at home tonight, then?" L. C. tried to sound casual but was holding his breath awaiting her reply.

"Yes, L. C., I'm staying home," she told him.

"Okay. Well, I'll let you go then," L. C. said, sounding relieved. He hung up then.

Kay was surprised that L. C. gave up so easily, but she was grateful that he did not try to call her again that evening. She and Jason were able to eat their dinner together on the couch in front of the TV in peace.

After dinner, Kay spoke with her friend Tana on the phone, and they decided to drive by Viktor's apartment one more time just to see if they could determine whether he had ever made it back home. Since Viktor still had not called, Kay was convinced that he was no longer romantically interested in her. The heart, however, is not so easily assuaged. Kay could not help but think about Viktor and how different he was from L. C. Underwood. Yet when Kay and Tana arrived at Viktor's apartment, they saw that his car was in the same place they had seen it over the previous weekend, as if it still had not been moved. Furthermore, some photos they had left him on Sunday were still stuck in his apartment door just as they had left them. Neither Kay nor Tana could come up with a rational explanation as to where Viktor could have gone in such a hurry without his car.

"Do you still think he just took off with someone?" Kay asked Tana on the way back to Kay's house.

By now, Tana was not so confident that Viktor was alright. "I don't know what to think. He must have left in a big hurry because he did not take that jacket he always wears or even shut his door all the way. ...But he'll show up. He always does." She tried to convince herself the whole disappearing act was just Viktor being Viktor – taking off on a whim with some friend or other. "He'll show back up," she assured Kay with more certainty than she felt.

Kay had no way of knowing then, but Viktor would never return to Salisbury. He would return to his family home in Sweden a little more than a month later, however, to the place where he had grown up and where his family still resided. He would return home in a body bag with my initials on it.

CHAPTER THREE

"Then when lust hath conceived, it bringeth forth sin: and sin, when it is finished, bringeth forth death." (James 1:15)

Kay's alarm clock chirped the next morning, which was Thursday, the ninth day of December. Kay dressed and drove herself to work as usual. About an hour after she arrived, Kay was surprised to see Mr. Paul Brown, her mother's boss, arrive at the school with a lady who was a friend and co-worker of Catherine Miller's. They had come for Kay.

"Wh-what's wrong?" Kay asked shakily, an uncertain knot forming in her chest.

Paul Brown, touching her gently on the shoulder, said, "Mrs. Weden, did you happen to speak with your mother this morning?"

"No, I haven't. Why?"

"Your mother was not at work today. If it were anyone else, we wouldn't be as concerned. But as you know, your mother never misses work, and she is never late. We were concerned about her, so we called the sheriff's department. We asked them to go by and check on her at her house." A sick feeling of dread completely washed over Kay. She grabbed her purse and got into Paul Brown's car.

Paul Brown drove them to Catherine Miller's home at 118 Larch Road, less than a mile from where Kay and Jason lived. Upon their arrival at Kay's mother's house, they were met with blue lights from Rowan County Sheriff's Office cruisers parked in front. Kay's heart was pounding, and she felt nauseated. But she managed to get out of the car, and then she walked quickly towards the house. She was stopped by one of the deputies. "Mrs. Weden, we can't get into the house because we don't have a key." Kay did not understand why they did not force the door open and go inside to check on her mother.

"I have a key," she told them, "but it's at my house just up the street."

The deputy drove Kay quickly to her house where she went inside to get her mother's house key. She picked up a key with one hand and reached for the phone with the other. For no known reason, Kay dialed L. C.'s house. There was no answer. She left a message on his answering machine, "L. C., something has happened to my mother." She laid the phone down and quickly returned to her mother's house.

Kay walked to the kitchen entrance, which she always used when she visited her mother. The first thing she noticed was that the storm door was not locked. Her mother always kept the screen door locked, and she would never unlock it unless she recognized whoever was at the door. But that was not possible. Kay could not imagine that anyone would want to harm her sweet little 77-year-old mother. Would they?

Suddenly, it dawned on Kay that if someone had done something to her mother, it had to be someone her mother knew. Not only that, but the face of a specific person flashed through her mind like an electrical shock as soon as she took hold of the storm door handle. *It was the face of L. C. Underwood.* She felt sick as she recalled the content of his phone calls the evening before. She tried to tell herself that L. C. would not have murdered her mother if he cared for Kay at all, that he was not capable of such a horrible crime. But that did not ring quite true.

Kay pulled open the unlocked storm door, her hand still trembling with the unexpected shock. She needed to unlock the heavier door next that separated her and the deputies from her mother's kitchen. But Kay's key would not fit the lock. She had mistakenly picked up her own extra house key instead of her mother's house key. She nearly collapsed from the stress.

"Please, just go on in – just force the door if you have to," Kay told the deputies. So, they did. With what seemed like a small effort, Deputy Chad Moose forced open the locked door. Kay wanted to go inside, but the deputies would not allow it. She was made to stand out of the way while deputies went inside. The first deputy to arrive on the scene followed Deputy Moose to the door and waited behind him. Deputy Moose stepped into the kitchen and paused at the gruesome scene before him. There was a lot of blood. The smell of it plus the acrid stench of burning beans on the stove nearly took his breath.

He scanned the entire room quickly. The electronic keypad on the wall indicated that the alarm had been disarmed, not activated.

He reached down to feel for a pulse on the body that slumped by the door he had just entered. There was no pulse, no signs of breathing. Her skin was cold to the touch. Her plump, grandmotherly body was slumped awkwardly against the stark white refrigerator, half-sitting, half-lying, in a scarlet gelatin pool. Two gunshot wounds were immediately apparent on the top of her head, gaping angrily among her thinning white hair.

The blood spatter was an explosion of crimson fireworks that had burst in a circular pattern on the side of the refrigerator, above her head. The narrow rivulets of blood that trickled down from the explosion were fairly dry, but slightly sticky in the heavier areas. Fragments of scalp, hair, and droplets of blood were splattered on the wall behind, and on the ceiling, above Mrs. Miller. Upon closer inspection, a smearing of blood across the floor spread from a point near the kitchen wall forward to the point where Mrs. Miller's left foot slid as she apparently collapsed slowly, sliding down to the floor, coming to a final rest on her buttocks with her legs stretched out into a "V" in front.

She wore a solid pink dress with long sleeves, accessorized with a strand of gold and white beads. Her eyeglasses had slid down on her nose, nearly having slipped off her face. Her eyes were partially open, and her mouth was moderately open. On her feet were red, yellow, and green flat-soled house shoes over her light beige hose. Her right arm was resting on her right thigh, and her left arm was on the floor to her side. A white plastic button was on the floor to the left of the body in the center of the floor. The button was determined later to have originated from a kitchen towel that should have been hanging on the handle of the refrigerator door.

From the downward angle and location of the wounds on the top of her head, it appeared that Catherine Miller had been pushed or knocked backward, or that she had stumbled as she retreated backward and had fallen or was in the process of falling when she was shot twice in the top of the head. The shooter likely was standing over her when he fired both shots.

Still simmering on the kitchen stove was Catherine Miller's simple dinner, a pan of navy beans, which had dried out and scorched over the low heat. She never had the opportunity to partake of the last meal she prepared. On the table was the December 8th edition of the *Salisbury Post*, which was delivered shortly before she arrived home the evening before. The television was set on a regional news channel, the volume at a low to normal range.

Deputy Moose backed out of the house carefully, notified his supervisor, and called for the Detectives.

Catherine Miller, age 77, was pronounced dead at the scene.

Detectives found atypical signs of disarray in the living room of Catherine Miller's home. While most items were untouched, the magazines on the coffee table had been slung off and onto the floor, in what appeared to be a single swiping motion. A plump bank bag lying in plain sight on a chair was not opened and not moved. A drawer full of silver flatware was pulled open, but no pieces were missing.

In the bedrooms, some drawers had been pulled out of dressers and the contents were sitting on the floor. Oddly enough, the contents were not dumped haphazardly; they were stacked neatly. And again, no items were missing. An extensive quantity of jewelry, guns, and cash was still in the house. In fact, the only thing that seemed to be missing was Mrs. Miller's purse.

Several inferences could be made from the crime scene. First of all, robbery was clearly not a motive in this murder, as many items of value were in plain view inside the residence and had not been taken. The items that were disturbed were moved in such a way as to appear "staged." Neither was sexual assault a motive, as the autopsy would later reveal. This motive screamed personal.

Kay was in shock, overwhelmed by grief. Jason, on the other hand, reacted to the news with a mixture of anger and grief. He could not merely sit and do nothing. He got into his car and began driving, accompanied by his friend Mikkel, eventually finding themselves at L. C. Underwood's home. He was, after all, a cop, and they needed answers. Surely L. C. would do what he could to help them in such an awful crisis.

"Someone murdered my grandmother!" Jason told L. C.

"Really? That's terrible," L. C. said, rather calmly.

Awkward pauses followed. Jason later realized that L. C. never asked if Kay was safe or how she was doing.

"Well, uh, do they know who did it?" L. C. asked.

Jason shook his head.

"What all are they doing there?" he asked.

"I don't know. But there's still a lot of cars over there," Jason said.

"Well, um, do they have dogs? You know, like tracking dogs?"

"I don't know."

"Well, uh, does Kay know you two are here?" L. C. asked. Jason and Mikkel shook their heads.

"Why don't you call her and let her know," L. C. suggested to Jason. Jason walked over to L. C.'s phone, picked up the receiver and dialed his mother.

"Where are you?" she asked Jason, nearly frantic.

"We're at L. C.'s," he told her.

"What?" Kay demanded. She felt sick all over again.

"We're over at L. C.'s. He told me to ask you if they have dogs there."

"*Dogs?*" Kay asked, confused.

"Like tracking dogs. L. C. asked if they had tracking dogs at Grandma's house."

"No. Why would they have those?" Kay asked.

"I don't know. L. C. just told me to ask you."

"Jason, you need to leave. I don't care where you go. Just leave. Leave *now*," Kay told him firmly. The last time Jason was there, L. C. pointed a loaded gun right at him. Kay had screamed at L. C., who claimed to have been asleep and awoke suddenly to see Jason in his bedroom, supposing him to be a burglar. But L. C. had not been asleep at all; he was feigning being dead in his recliner in one of his faux suicidal performances. He knew who Jason was and that it was Jason and Kay that were standing in the room with him at the time.

"Just get out of there now, son," she pleaded.

"Alright Mom." Jason hung up the phone. L. C. never asked how Kay was doing nor did he ask to speak to her. Jason and Mikkel left. L. C., this man who proclaimed to love Kay "so very much" and wanted to "hold her in his arms forever" never called Kay nor left her even a brief message of sympathy or concern following her mother's death.

When Jason arrived home, Kay asked him why he had gone to L. C.'s house.

"I don't know, Mom; he's a cop. I thought he might know something. Why didn't you want me over there? Why did you want me to leave like that?"

"I – I just don't want you over there. I don't want you to go over there again. Do you understand, son? Not ever." She meant business.

"Okay Mom, okay."

"What did L. C. say to you?" Kay asked.

"Nothing really. Just what I asked you about the dogs."

"I still don't know why he would ask that. Did he say anything else when you told him your grandmother had been killed?"

"No, no, not really. I'm tired. It's just been the most awful day, Mom."

"I know, I know. I'm so sorry, Jason. But your grandmother loved you very much. Very much!"

"Mom? L. C. did ask me something," Jason remembered. "He had some cash and asked me if I needed any money. He offered to give me some money."

"He did?" Kay asked, surprised. L. C. had never given Jason money, to her knowledge. He was way too stingy, and he certainly did not care for Jason. In fact, he was jealous and resentful of Jason, referring to him frequently as a spoiled brat, and worse titles than that behind Kay's back.

"Yeah. He, he asked me if I needed any cash for anything. I told him I didn't need any." Kay recalled that her mother's purse was missing, undoubtedly stolen by her killer. In all probability there would have been some cash in the purse, as was her mother's habit to carry generally. Was it possible that L. C. could have been offering Jason money that was inside his grandmother's stolen purse? The ramifications of this possibility were far too outrageous for a broken, grieving daughter to contemplate on the worst day of her life thus far, the day her sweet mother was found brutally shot to death. She brushed aside her suspicious thoughts. Surely she would have answers soon.

The autopsy conducted the following day at the University of North Carolina at Chapel Hill confirmed that Catherine Miller had indeed expired as a direct result of two gunshot wounds to the head. Forensic analysis revealed that she had been shot at close range, within approximately twelve inches, by a .38 caliber Colt revolver. L. C. Underwood carried a snub-nose .38 caliber Colt Detective Special, which he had obtained from a previous employer, the Lincoln County Sheriff's Office. When investigators asked to see the Colt, L. C. told them he had given it to one of his foster "brothers" in Ohio, along with his .22 caliber weapons: a revolver and a rifle. The "brother" adamantly denied ever having received a weapon of any kind from L. C. Underwood. Investigators later learned that Viktor Gunnarsson was killed with a .22 caliber weapon just like the one L. C. had but claimed he had given to his foster brother. None of the suspected weapons were ever located.

A number of latent fingerprints were lifted from inside the Catherine Miller residence. Unfortunately, all of the lifts that were able to be identified were made by Catherine Miller. Unaware that we had not found any prints belonging to anyone other than Catherine Miller, L. C. later told several individuals that he expected us to find his fingerprints inside her house, and that it meant nothing because he had been there on several occasions. L. C. also claimed to have taken a shower at Catherine Miller's after completing some yard work for her on one occasion, and that would explain any of his body hair that might be found in her bathtub.

On the same day Catherine Miller was found murdered, an employee of the Salisbury Housing Authority and his crew were blowing leaves off a sidewalk in front of a public housing apartment building when they found items bearing Catherine Miller's name from her wallet: three credit cards, an insurance card, an AARP card, and a blood type card. A few feet away, they also found a flexible band ring-watch which Kay later identified as her mother's.

A few hours later, another citizen of Salisbury found Catherine Miller's wallet a few blocks away on Horah Street in a low-income neighborhood well known to the Salisbury Police for its illegal drugs and other criminal activity. There was no cash inside the wallet.

Analysts in the Latent Evidence Section of the SBI Crime Lab carefully examined each of the recovered items belonging to Catherine Miller. Not even a single fingerprint was found. The cards had all been wiped clean. Whomever had tossed them had known enough about forensic evidence to remove any traces of latent evidence such as fingerprints as well as DNA.

Investigators with the Rowan County Sheriff's Office, assisted by the North Carolina State Bureau of Investigation (SBI), had been working the case for a week before Viktor Gunnarsson was reported missing to the Salisbury Police Department by his apartment manager on December 15th. Lead Detective Terry Agner and S.B.I. Agent Don Gale were exploring every possible angle in the Catherine Miller murder when it occurred to Kay Weden shortly after her mother's funeral that she still had not heard a word from Viktor Gunnarsson, and that perhaps she should mention it to the investigators. The investigators quickly connected the dots, and Kay Weden was found to be the common denominator between Viktor Gunnarsson's disappearance and Catherine Miller's murder.

CHAPTER FOUR

**"My heart is sore pained within me: and the
terrors of death are fallen upon me."
(Psalm 55:4)**

Detective Agner and Agent Gale began to visualize the
ugly picture that was forming as they collected pieces of
the puzzle from Kay Weden and others. Kay's tumultuous
relationship with Salisbury Police Officer L. C. Underwood
was more than a little disturbing. It was about that time that
I entered the picture as well, with the discovery of Viktor
Gunnarsson's murdered body. Along with S.B.I. Agent
Steve Wilson who was assigned to assist me on the Watauga
County end, Detective Agner, Agent Gale, and I formed an
investigative team that would bind us together for the next
four years and beyond, united in a single cause to bring to
justice one of our own: the man who took it upon himself to
shed innocent blood, taking the life of at least one, but in all
likelihood two unsuspecting adults, to terrorize an innocent
single mother and her adolescent son, and to tarnish with
evil the badge meant for good, to which we had all sworn an
oath to protect and serve others.

It took months to uncover all the circumstantial and
physical evidence required to charge and convict L. C.
Underwood of the First Degree Murder and First Degree
Kidnapping of Viktor Gunnarsson. Although I was the
lead investigator and the case was assigned to me, it was
absolutely a team effort. Don, Steve, Terry, and I worked

around the clock. We worked weekends and holidays. We traveled far and near tracking down anything and anyone who could help us put the facts together in a manner in which we could present them to a jury of twelve reasonable and objective jurors. I spent more time than I would have liked away from my family, but they seemed to understand, especially when the long hours and all the turning over of rocks paid off.

We had discovered sufficient evidence, not only consisting of the probable cause to arrest L. C. Underwood, but to convict. The extensive trial was a high profile one in our rural county. The international element of intrigue involving the assassination of Sweden's prime minister also attracted the interest of the national and international media. Sheriff Lyons and I were in regular demand for interviews in statements both before and after the trial.

As if the facts that the murderer was a police officer and one of his victims a possible assassin were not enough, the State of North Carolina vs. Lamont Claxton Underwood was the first case in the entire state to admit mitochondrial DNA analysis into a criminal trial, second in the country only to the State of Tennessee the previous year. This fact was of particular interest in a dawning age of fascination with forensic evidence.

Forensic science itself was not a new course of study. The first known legal autopsies were performed in Italy as early as 1302 to determine cause of death, and the microscope was invented by Hans and Zacharias Janssen in 1590. In 1835, the first known comparison of bullets was conducted. In the 1880s, scientists began to the study of fingerprints as forensic evidence. Francis Galton, as a result of his research, computed that an individual's fingerprints had only one chance in sixty-four billion of being like the fingerprints of another individual. It was the same year that the first crime was solved through fingerprint analysis.

Human blood types were discovered by Karl Landsteiner in 1900. Dr. Edmond Locard, a French scientist, is attributed with the creation of the first crime laboratory in 1910, and it was Dr. Locard who proposed the concept of trace evidence, proving that almost everything leaves some type of trace. I learned in my basic investigative training that no one enters a scene without bringing something with him, and no one leaves a scene without taking something from it. This concept was key to L. C. Underwood's ultimate verdict in the Gunnarsson case.

By the late 1900s, the advances of forensic science in the areas of DNA (deoxyribonucleic acid) analysis and identification had expanded seemingly overnight. The method of DNA profiling began at the University of Leicester in the United Kingdom, about the same time that scientist, Kary Mullis, developed the polymerase chain reaction process of DNA analysis which resulted in unprecedented accuracy in analyzing even the tiniest samples of DNA that criminal investigators collect, such as a droplet of saliva left on a discarded cigarette butt. Mitochondrial DNA differed from traditional or nuclear DNA in that there is generally no change from parent to child, and because of that fact, it is often used in the tracking of ancestry, but can also be extremely valuable in our area of criminal forensics.

When Viktor Gunnarsson was bound, gagged, and shoved into the trunk of the Monte Carlo, he had struggled and squirmed to the point that at least seventeen of his head hairs were loosed from his head and ground into the fiber of the carpeted trunk mat. In a futile effort to destroy any physical evidence, Underwood had taken the car to have it professionally cleaned just after he returned home from his late-night drive to the mountains, to the extent that he had the car cleaning company shampoo the carpeted trunk mat. While it undoubtedly did result in the destruction of a great deal of physical evidence, Viktor Gunnarsson's head hairs remained for SBI Crime Lab Analyst John Bendure to discover many months after the fact in a manner that only divine intervention could explain.

S.B.I. Crime Lab Analysts John Bendure, Troy Hamlin, and others had worked relentlessly trying to retrieve any existing physical evidence there might be in or on L. C. Underwood's personal property. The trunk mats from both vehicles had been searched thoroughly with tapings, combings, vacuumings, and other manners known to collect any existing hair, fiber, or any other type of trace evidence, all to no avail. The analysts had spent hours upon hours looking under microscopes and various lighting sources in an attempt to find trace evidence on the trunk mats from both of L. C.'s vehicles, without success. What happened next was nothing short of miraculous.

Having exhausted every known method of discovering any trace evidence, Agent John Bendure began the process of packaging the trunk mats to return to me. As John held up the trunk mat from L. C.'s Monte Carlo one final time and began to roll and fold it for shipping, he saw in the daylight at a particular angle what he had been unable to see before… hair. Seventeen human head hairs to be precise. Moreover, it was clear that the hairs did *not* belong to L. C. Underwood.

I recalled the phone conversation clearly. It came after many other conversations with John Bendure, and we were easily on a first name basis by this point.

"Paula, I've compared the hairs I found to the known head hair of Viktor Gunnarsson, and microscopically, they are a perfect match." I kept asking John to be sure I understood exactly what he was telling me. I think he was about as pleased at his finding as I was. I said a silent prayer of thanksgiving to God for his divine intervention in this case and for the diligence of John and the many other analysts that worked relentlessly in the crime lab demonstrated every single day on the job.

In the end, with the help of both the North Carolina State Bureau of Investigation as well as the Federal Bureau of

Investigation crime labs, we were able to take advantage of the recent developments in the field of mitochondrial DNA analysis in order to prove that the DNA extracted from the head hair found in L. C.'s trunk lined up perfectly with Viktor Gunnarsson's known mitochondrial DNA. It was definitely the kind of thing everyone seemed to be watching on prime-time television.

There was other physical evidence in the case as well, including a man-sized shoe print discovered on the underside of the Monte Carlo's trunk lid. We did not find Viktor's shoes with which to compare it, but who leaves a shoe print on the underside of a trunk lid if not from inside it with the lid closed? Also admitted into evidence was a piece of electrical tape found at the scene where Viktor Gunnarsson's body was found which matched in twenty-some physical characteristics a piece of electrical tape from Underwood's clothes dryer in the utility room of his home... also a bit of divine intervention occurred in that finding as well. The physical evidence consisting of the hair, the shoe print, and the tape were not exactly overwhelming in the way of physical evidence, but it was enough.

The circumstantial evidence, on the other hand, was overwhelming, at least in my perspective. Strong circumstantial evidence demonstrated that L. C. Underwood had been terrorizing Kay Weden for many months, beginning shortly after she tried to end their relationship. L. C. could not – *would* not – accept personal rejection on any level.

Unwanted and abandoned by his own parents as a young child, he lived briefly with a physically and mentally abusive uncle before Uncle George also abandoned him, albeit at a local orphanage, the Methodist Children's Home in Winston-Salem, North Carolina, where L. C. lived out the rest of his childhood in bitterness and anger. I felt sorry for the little boy that no one wanted, but nothing L. C. experienced as a child could justify his outrageous conduct as a grown man; a grown man who well knew the difference between right and wrong but disregarded the former in favor of his own cruel machinations and selfish gratifications.

As a young adult, he longed for a personal and intimate relationship of his own but was simply incapable of it. No one seemed to respect him, at least not in the fashion that he thought was due him. While other children were collected from the Children's Home on weekends and holidays by prospective couples or family members, L. C. was frequently left behind. He learned to take his frustration out on different kinds of animals to which he had access and developed a reputation for torturing cats and dogs in particular. He was disciplined for setting or attempting to set fires in random locations. The more rejected he felt, the crueler he became. It was a vicious and calamitous cycle.

With adulthood came his exposure to law enforcement, and while it should have been a positive influence on his life, it was the appeal of the authority and power which drew him to the field as a career choice. He was one of the rotten apples that gave the vast majority of dedicated law enforcement officers a bad name. The rigor of the paramilitary organizational structure with its clear lines of delineation and chain of command appealed to L. C.'s familiarity with the rigid structure and stern discipline of the Children's Home – the structure of which he had been tragically deprived as a small child with his neglectful, dysfunctional, and self-destructive parents.

Thus L. C. applied for employment with a small police department in the foothills of western North Carolina, and the Chief of Police there took a liking to him. Thus, his career in law enforcement began at the North Wilkesboro Police Department. Miraculously, at a time when discipline against law enforcement officers was largely handled in-house with precious little documentation on paper, L. C. was able to continue stalking the night, wearing a police uniform, a badge, and a gun with little supervision.

Although he survived a career in law enforcement for nineteen years, he could not stay out of trouble. More often than not, L. C.'s trouble involved women with whom he had become intimately involved, with a couple of complaints of excessive or unnecessary uses of force thrown in for good measure.

In other areas of the job, however, L. C. excelled. Suffering from a severe case of obsessive-compulsive disorder, he was neat and organized to a fault. Individuals who knew him personally or worked with him regularly poured forth accounts of his excessively polished and shined uniform, his immaculate patrol car, and certainly his dust-free and clutter-free home. I heard about all of his habits from ironing the fringe on his throw-rugs to coating the hoses in his patrol car with Armor-All so that everyone could hear him coming from a mile away.

In a search of his home, I saw for myself how every item in his cabinets was alphabetized with labels facing forward, how every single one of his starched and pressed dress shirts hung in the same direction, equally distanced apart, and how the eight or so pairs of identical dress shoes bore shoe trees inside and rubber bands around the tassels to prevent fraying. But it was more than just a neatness obsession; an obvious need for control was exhibited.

Everything that was framed and hung on his wall reflected some type of accomplishment, no matter how minor, even informal thank you notes or news articles that only mentioned his name in passing. He had obviously had them all professionally matted and framed. His home, as well as his two cars, screamed extreme *narcissism*.

On the job, L. C. was consistently punctual. His reports were neatly handwritten, and he was fairly thorough. So rather than being weeded out of the profession, when the heat became too much at one agency due to his personal problems, L. C. would simply move on to another law enforcement position elsewhere.

More than one agency head would provide him with a favorable reference, most likely just to get rid of him easily, and he would move on to become the problem of some other chief or sheriff. As a relatively young female law enforcement officer charging upwardly against the glass ceiling in a male-dominated profession, I was appalled at what I discovered had occurred – or rather had failed to occur – as I searched through uncharacteristically thin personnel files and interviewed several of 'the good old boys' who comprised the autonomous group of some of

L. C. Underwood's former supervisors and department heads who had enabled him to continue as a law enforcement officer by failing to address or even document his issues.

At the end of one of the days we spent attempting to gather information, Steve said, "That's the same old good ole boys' network for you."

I well understood what we were encountering, but I did not care for it at all.

"I never wanted to become part of that," I told Steve candidly.

"Well, biologically, you may not qualify," he joked, referring to my gender. "But you know you want in, with all that power and everything, where they say, you scratch my back and I'll scratch yours..."

"Right," I said facetiously. "Next to getting a massage from Edward Scissorhands, that'd be my second favorite thing." Steve laughed.

Years later, when I had worked my way through the ranks to become a member of the command staff myself and ultimately a Chief of Police in another city, I would recall how L. C. Underwood had slithered through his career due in part to a lack of transparency and accurate recordkeeping by his former commanders, and I would vow never to get caught up in those kinds of "good old boy" politics. For better or for worse, I was determined to lead with integrity and professionalism, even in the face of political strongholds that would seemingly never be torn down.

In L. C. Underwood's era, I could clearly see a disturbing pattern that would recur for two decades, as he went from working as an officer at North Wilkesboro Police Department to Newton Police Department, then to Lincoln County Sheriff's Department, and finally to Salisbury Police Department where his problems finally came to a head. At some point along the way, L. C. stopped fighting his demons and joined them on the same side.

L. C.'s natural good looks, cunning ways, and the natural trust that was granted with the police badge drew more than one unassuming young lady to him. But his superficial charm soon gave way to jealousy, possessiveness, and violence. Unfortunately, L. C. Underwood had caused many of a young woman to suffer, and I had met and interviewed the vast majority of them. For years afterward, a few of his victims in particular would come to my mind from time to time.

L. C. met Patty Lewis and began dating her when he worked for the Lincoln County Sheriff's Office in the City of Lincolnton, North Carolina. Patty was far kinder to L. C. than he deserved. Little things set off his temper, such as Patty not having cigarettes at her apartment for him to smoke (although she herself did not smoke) or her taking a phone call from a work client after hours (at which L. C. promptly grabbed the phone, cursed the client, and slammed the phone down). It took little else to set him off, and his temper instilled in Patty a fear that remained for an awfully long time.

On another occasion, Lamont and Patty went to visit a friend of Lamont's who happened to be an attorney. The attorney passed out beers for everyone, and even though Patty did not normally drink alcohol, she accepted the beer so as not to appear rude. But Lamont grabbed the beer out of her hands and told her loudly enough for everyone to hear,

"Sluts drink." He embarrassed her on multiple occasions. Their relationship continued to worsen, like so many others L. C. was involved in. Patty finally told L. C. it was over. But it was not over for him.

After managing to avoid him for a few weeks after an attempted breakup, Patty accepted an invitation to go out with friends, unaware that L. C. was watching her every move. She came home to find L. C. waiting for her. He forced his way into her apartment and beat her severely with a wooden chair he picked up and swung like a baseball bat. He grabbed a heavy potted plant and smashed it on top of her head, dirt landing in her eyes and all over her clothes, and nearly knocking her out cold. He ripped her sweater, yanking at it as he screamed obscenities at her. He shoved her down onto the floor, straddled her, and began strangling her. I thought many times over the years of what he did to Patty, and I knew he would do the same to me if he ever got half a chance.

Patty cried as she described to me in detail what L. C. did to her that night. "I went black for a minute, and he would let up. Then he would start choking me all over again, and I'd black out again. He kept doing that…over and over! He…he took his .38 revolver from his holster and stuck the barrel between my eyes… He called me a terrible name and declared furiously, 'You're gonna die!' I *knew* he wanted to kill me more than anything else in that moment, and I knew there was a good chance I would die. …Detective May, do you know what that is like? To know, to feel with your whole being, that someone wants to kill you?" But she did not wait for my answer. She was not yet finished sharing what L. C. said to her before he finally left.

"He told me he was going to be riding along with another officer that night – all night – and that if I called the police, he would hear it on the radio, and he, he told me he would kill me. And he meant it!" She never called the police.

Then there was Monica.

"We hadn't been dating but a few months when he started talking marriage," she said. "But I was afraid."

"What made you afraid, specifically?"

"His volatile temper, for one. One night when L. C. wasn't working, we got into an argument. I can't remember what it was over, probably nothing because it took nothing much of anything to set him off. He got so mad so fast. Anyway, since he was a detective, he wore, like, plain clothes, ya know? Like you are wearing?" I nodded. "Well, he always wore his loaded revolver on his belt. We got to arguing and he shoved me down on the floor, and he pulled his gun out of his belt and pointed it at my head! He sat on top of me, down on the floor, and pressed his gun – and I know it was loaded – against my forehead... I can still remember the feel of it right here [touching her forehead]...and he said 'I'm going to kill you! Then I'm going to kill myself!' Detective May, he meant it! I have never been so scared in all my life!"

I saw that Monica's hands were balled into fists and her knuckles had turned white.

"I know it's not easy reliving those memories, but it's very important," I said, encouraging her to go on.

"I know... I begged him to please stop, to please put the gun away, and when he finally did, I begged him to leave me alone." He just stayed on top of me – it seemed like hours although I'm sure it wasn't that long – and he finally rolled off of me. Then he just started crying and then tried to apologize. I was just... shocked... I couldn't believe what had just happened, that he had just done that to me." Unfortunately, it was not the only time he threatened or assaulted Monica, and when she tried to break up with L. C., he stalked her.

When Monica eventually began dating the man she would later marry, L. C. spray-painted obscenities about her in red paint on the outside of her parents' home. He did the same with the next woman, Linda, with whom he became involved; only that time he spray-painted "Linda is a whore" on the outside of the church she attended. L. C. threatened Linda's life and assaulted her as well. He was both mentally and physically abusive, and he was determined to terrorize anyone who rejected him. Narcissistic and extremely possessive, he simply could not take rejection in any form, but particularly not from women.

After three failed marriages and several other failed relationships, L. C. had seemingly learned nothing by the time he became involved – and later obsessed – with Kay Weden. For three long years, he made Kay's life a living nightmare. Among the many sordid acts he committed against her was his red spray-paint modus operandi, spraying threats and obscenities on both her car and home. As the forensic evidence would later prove, L. C. also threatened Kay in anonymous letters he sent to Kay as well as having made (and having employed another man to make) anonymous threatening phone calls to Kay. He feigned suicide attempts to upset and manipulate her. Then there was the mortifying scene in Bogart's Restaurant in Salisbury which culminated with L. C. dumping a glass of iced tea in Kay's lap and the manager calling the police.

L. C. lied incessantly. In fact, it seemed he was incapable of telling the truth to anyone. I was reminded of something my Grandpa Earl used to say.

"He'd rather climb a tree to tell a lie than stand on the ground and tell the truth."

L. C. was quite the tree climber.

L. C. perpetuated many lies about his so-called mother Barbara, whom he called *Bobbie*, who lived in Ohio. One of these lies was that he told several individuals that she had died of cancer and that he alone had paid all of her medical and funeral bills. The truth was that, first of all, the woman to which he referred was neither his mother, nor his stepmother, nor his adoptive mother; secondly, she was not dead nor in the process of dying; thirdly, she never had cancer in any form; and fourthly, L. C. Underwood never gave her any money for any reason. Yet he lamented to a number of friends and co-workers that same lie or some variation of it, all in an attempt to elicit sympathy or to explain away his bad mood or bad behavior. As expected, the people he told believed him and offered him sympathy in one form or another.

Lying, however, was only one of the sins in L. C.'s repertoire. I had no doubt that it was L. C. who shot into Jason's bedroom one night while he was in bed sleeping. It was another case of divine intervention since Jason and Kay had rearranged his furniture that very day, a fact which L. C. was unaware of, and which ultimately saved Jason's life. Had Jason been in bed as L. C. recalled the furniture arrangement, he likely would have suffered a .22 caliber gunshot wound to the top of his head.

L. C. resented both Kay's son and her mother, not only because Kay was close to them emotionally, but also because both disapproved of Kay's having any type of relationship withL. C.

Unfortunately for them all, L. C. well knew how both Catherine and Jason really felt about him, and as he saw it, both Jason Weden and Catherine Miller stood in the way of his relationship with Kay. What Jason, Catherine, and Kay failed to realize at the time was the depth of L. C.'s resentment and the lack of conscience L. C. possessed. No one at that time could have known the evil that lurked in L. C.'s mind.

The time came, however, when he turned his unwanted attention towards me.

CHAPTER FIVE

"And shall not God avenge his own elect, which cry day and night unto him..." (Luke 18:7)

The conclusion of the Gunnarsson murder trial was by no means the conclusion of our involvement with L. C. Underwood. Our team of four investigators fully expected to go through another extensive trial in the near future in which L. C. Underwood would face similar charges for the murder of Catherine Miller. We were mentally and professionally prepared to do it all again, this time in the Superior Court of Rowan County. Whereas Viktor Gunnarsson's murder occurred in Watauga County, Catherine Miller was murdered in Rowan County, thus the Rowan County Courthouse would be the location of the trial, and District Attorney Bill Kenerly would prosecute the case there with assistance as needed from our District Attorney Tom Rusher and his Assistant District Attorney Jerry Wilson, both of whom argued before the Court expertly and successfully in the Gunnarsson murder trial. Another consideration was that, over time, necessary witnesses moved away from the area or could become unavailable for various reasons. Additionally, key witnesses could even die.

While we had little in the way of actual physical evidence in the Catherine Miller murder case, I had the overwhelming circumstantial evidence and all the confidence in the world that a jury would convict Underwood as quickly and easily as they had done in the Gunnarsson case. Furthermore, a trial in the Miller case would not require the detailed organization of facts that our trial had required because it was already done. In fact, as I saw it, the transcripts of the trial we had just completed would constitute an easy outline for Mr. Kenerly and his staff to use in their trial. The witnesses could all be easily scheduled to testify again while their memories were fresh and their confidence high. Even jurors in our case expressed after the trial that they wanted to see Underwood brought to trial for the murder of Catherine Miller.

Above all this, though, I wanted resolution and closure for both Kay and Jason; Kay who had been brutally robbed of her loving, supportive mother, and Jason who had lost his precious grandmother. They had suffered months, nay, even years of unwarranted and absolute terror at the hand of L. C. Underwood, and they deserved to have some justice, at least as much justice as our best efforts could give them. Our team and I had not worked so hard and so incessantly for all this time to quit the race just before we reached the finish line.

Detective Terry Agner, Agents Don Gale and Steve Wilson, and I were reenergized by Underwood's conviction and all fired up for another trial. Additionally, we had one more shot at the death penalty, and if anyone I had ever investigated in my entire career was deserving of a death sentence, it was L. C. Underwood. I was convinced that Kay, especially, would have no peace as long as he was living, even if he were behind bars for the rest of his natural wicked life.

"It's too bad he didn't get the death penalty," Lieutenant Stout stated as he joined the four of us in the prosecutor's office after the trial, "but you all did everything you could do. Maybe you will get another shot at the death penalty in the Miller case."

"Maybe so," Don answered. "It would only be fitting for the cruel way he took each of their two lives."

"Being tied up in a trunk of a stranger's car for two hours in the freezing winter is certainly not the way *I* want to go," Terry commented.

"Me either," I agreed, "not that I can think of a really *good* way to die."

"Oh, sure there is," Lieutenant Stout replied. "I'd be happy to just slip away quietly, while I was sleeping in my own bed at home."

"Well, yeah, if we had a choice. I think I'd just like to skip death entirely and go by way of the Rapture," I said.

"There ya go," Steve said. "I like her plan better."

"If you know where you're headed, we can all go that way," I reminded them.

"I intend to live forever, or at least die trying," Don said wittily.

Then he added, "We can only hope that L. C. will be living the rest of *his* life behind bars."

If only. I think we would all feel better if he at least had another lengthy sentence tacked onto his current one. Also, who could say what the Court of Appeals would do when he started the seemingly endless series of those attempts in the Gunnarsson case? I knew the many possibilities, the things that could go wrong. The reality was that Underwood had any number of avenues to exhaust by way of appeal before I could ever rest easy. Even if he never won a single appeal, he still was eligible for parole before his full sentence would be served. At some point in time, in all likelihood, L. C. Underwood would walk out of prison a free man, albeit an angry, bitter, and vengeful one. He must be tried and convicted for murdering Catherine Miller in the first degree. He simply must.

Kay recalls that SBI Agent Don Gale assured her on the same day that L. C. was sentenced for murdering Viktor Gunnarsson, before anyone even left the courthouse, that L. C. would be charged and tried for her mother's brutal murder. She told me that she recalls it so vividly because she clung to Don's words for days after the trial in our case was over.

Don made those assurances to Kay Weden in good faith, based on what he was directly told. We had discussed the case at length not only with the Watauga County prosecutors but also with Rowan County D.A. Bill Kenerly and his staff on a number of occasions throughout the entire investigation. Don had every reason to assume Kenerly would try L. C. Underwood sooner rather than later, as did the rest of us.

"Hey there. Guess what?" Steve (SBI Agent Steve Wilson) asked me when he walked into the Investigations Division one midweek afternoon.

"Let's see… the fifth dentist changed his mind, and now they're *all* recommending Trident gum?"

"Hmm, nope. That's not it," he said. "Although if that were true, they'd have to change the commercials."

"Bad news?" I asked.

"Well, it isn't *good* news. …He's not going to do it," Steve said, finally.

"Who's not going to do what?" I asked. But then I suddenly knew what he meant.

"Bill Kenerly is not going to prosecute L. C. Underwood for the Miller murder," Steve announced.

"You aren't kidding?" I asked hopefully.

"I wish I was, but no, I'm not," he said soberly.

"Why? What did he say?"

"He basically just said he was not going to prosecute."

"I can't believe it," I said.

"Well, I can't either, Paula," Steve responded. "But it's his decision."

"I know it's his decision," I said. "I mean, I can't believe he would *make* that decision, the decision not to take him to trial. He very brutally killed that sweet little lady inside her own home. In cold blood," I added.

"I heard," Steve said.

"Does Terry know?" I asked.

"Yes. He was with Don when Kenerly told them."

"Has he told Kay?" I asked. "Has anyone told her?"

"I don't know. Don said something about Kenerly putting it in a letter or something."

"You mean he isn't even going to tell her in person? To explain?"

"It didn't sound like it. But who knows?" Steve said.

I tried to think rationally. "Ok," I began again. "There must be something we're missing here. Surely there is a good reason or reasons for Kenerly to make such a decision, especially without talking to the four of us and to Tom at least..."

"My understanding is that he, Tom, and Jerry all discussed it – at length – and they decided it was best not to prosecute."

"Best for whom?" I asked.

"I don't know, really," Steve admitted. "But Don can probably explain it better than I can because he talked to Kenerly directly. Why don't you call and ask him?"

"I will. And I'm gonna ask Tom too. And Kenerly. It doesn't seem right, Steve. It doesn't seem fair to Kay. Or Jason. And we just proved that a jury would convict L. C.; they just did. I mean, *they literally just did*!"

"I heard that too." He was trying to lighten my darkening mood. "Maybe they feel that there isn't enough evidence, physical evidence I mean, to convict. Maybe he wants to wait and see if any additional evidence can be found."

"That's B.S., Steve, and you know it."

"I know it is, but I'm not the one making the decision."

"Well, maybe there needs to be some accountability accompanying that kind of discretion," I said, "and I'm not about to see this swept under the rug or fall through the cracks or, or whatever other bad metaphor applies in this situation."

"Go get 'em, girl," Steve replied.

"I'll let you know if I ever get any satisfactory answers," I said.

"I'll be standing by," Steve said.

Don was his typical laidback self on the phone.

"What's going on, Don?" I asked.

"Well, I assume you are referring to Bill Kenerly's decision not to indict L. C. in the Miller case," Don said.

"What is the problem?" I asked.

"Well, I can only tell you what he told me, and after listening to him, it makes sense, at least to some degree."

"Help it make sense to me then," I said. "Not that it's going to stop me from calling Kenerly myself, though."

"Well, you can call him, but you won't catch him today because he was leaving the office when I talked to him and he isn't coming back until next Wednesday," Don said.

"Alright," I said. "Then I want to be the first person to welcome him back when he returns – if Kay doesn't find out first," I added.

"Okay, Paula, but first hear me out."

"Alright; I'm listening."

"I have known Bill Kenerly a long time, and I have come to respect him a great deal. He does not make rash, emotional decisions, and he is an honorable man. I trust his judgment."

"That is good to know. That is what I've heard from others about him. He isn't just simply afraid to take a high-profile case to a jury trial or too busy to want to deal with such a long and drawn-out trial as ours?"

"Absolutely not. Paula, I know prosecutors like that, and I know you do as well, but that is not Bill Kenerly."

"Oh, alright. If you trust his judgment, I guess I want to trust it too."

"I really do. In any case, as you well know, L. C. has a lot of appeals ahead," Don continued.

"All the more reason to keep him behind bars on something unrelated," I replied. "At least they are unrelated in the sense that Viktor's kidnapping and murder on Friday night was separate and apart in time – a matter of days in fact – from Catherine Miller's. And the motivation was not exactly the same, although Kay, of course, was the common denominator."

"Yes. In *his* mind, each one of them had gotten in the way of his relationship with Kay. So, in that sense, the two cases *are* related, although you are correct in that it was not a continuation of events occurring the same day. But here's the thing: Kenerly thinks that if we try L. C. on Catherine's murder, it could give him twice the appeal opportunities, and if L. C. wins even one appeal in either case, it could result in getting both convictions thrown out – assuming he would get convicted in the Miller case."

"Don, I think it would be even easier to convict him in the Miller case than our case because Catherine Miller, unlike Viktor Gunnarsson, had no skeletons in her closet, nothing but good deeds in her past and compassion for others. Just a helpless and innocent victim of such a heinous crime. A jury would not take kindly to that."

"Maybe so, but it doesn't look like we're gonna get the chance to find out."

"What else? What other reasons did Kenerly give for not wanting to try L. C. for Catherine's murder?" I asked.

"Well, he didn't say a whole lot more than that," Don said. "He just doesn't think we have a strong enough case. Maybe you can get more out of him or your D.A.," he suggested.

"I'm gonna try," I assured him. If there was a legitimate reason – correction, if there was a *really good* reason – for not prosecuting L. C. Underwood for the cold-blooded, atrocious murder of Catherine Miller, then I would like to know what it was. Kay called frequently to me, Don, or Terry, asking questions. I believe that she felt that if she lost touch with us that we would forget her mother's murder. She need not have worried. None of us could forget, and even if we had tried, L. C. did his best to make certain that we did not.

He began the appeals process right away, but assuming he never won an appeal entitling to him a new trial, he would serve the majority of his sentence under the Fair Sentencing Act, legislation which was initiated by a committee appointed by Governor Jim Hunt to research problems with the correctional system. The Fair Sentencing Act was North Carolina's first effort to establish a presumptive sentencing law. It specifically applied to felony offenses that were committed between July 1, 1981 and September 30, 1994.

Even after the state adopted Structured Sentencing, the Fair Sentencing Act still applies to any crimes that occurred between the originally established dates. Therefore, when we went to trial in 1997 after indicting L. C. for kidnapping and murder and the Fair Sentencing Act had been replaced by Structured Sentencing, the State still had to operate under the sentencing guidelines of the Fair Sentencing Act, since the offenses were committed in 1993. First Degree Murder in North Carolina is punishable by one of only two options, and those are death (by lethal injection) or life imprisonment. Under each sentencing system, L. C.'s life sentence would be treated the same and would equate to only about twenty years. But his First Degree Kidnapping conviction would be treated differently under either of the two systems.

Judge Forrest Ferrell sentenced L. C. to forty years imprisonment for the kidnapping conviction, a class C crime. Under the Fair Sentencing Act, however, individuals with non-life sentences (for crimes other than Class A or B offenses) receive a jolly good treat called "Good Time," which amounts to a "credit" at a rate of day per day. In other words, due to Good Time earned, an inmate who does not commit a major infraction while in custody automatically gets his/her sentence cut in half. Additionally, inmates could earn even more credit called "Gain Time" or "Meritorious Time." Gain Time is earned by participating in certain programs during incarceration (which L. C. would likely complete), and Meritorious Time is earned for acts that are heroic or exemplary (which I doubted he would do, but which L. C. might con someone into thinking he had done, being the narcissist that the facts had revealed him to be.)

Mentally I began adding the number of years, as best I could estimate, that L. C. would likely spend in prison before becoming eligible for a parole hearing – that is, if he did not con his way out before then, or worse, escape. He would likely still be a well-conditioned, healthy man, capable of practically any evil deed upon his release; never mind the fact that he might figure a way to escape at any given time. The possibilities made my own blood run cold.

CHAPTER SIX

**"Oh that I had wings like a dove for then
would I fly away, and be at rest."
(Psalm 55:6)**

In the past several years, Tom Rusher had earned my confidence. Tom, our elected District Attorney in the 24th Judicial District, had successfully prosecuted a substantial number of serious felonies, a significant portion of them being cases I had personally investigated. I had found Tom to be brilliant in the courtroom. He would later author a nonfiction book entitled *Until He Is Dead: Capital Punishment in Western North Carolina History* (Parkway Publishing, 2003).

I trusted Tom's judgment for the most part, even if we did not agree on every small matter, but even more importantly, I trusted him to tell me the truth, as I still do.

"Yes, Paula. Indeed, Bill (Kenerly) and I had quite an extensive discussion on the question of whether Underwood should be prosecuted for the murder of Catherine Miller," Tom began.

"I'm not sure either of you can convince me that it is a bad idea," I told Tom honestly, "not that it's my decision to make," I added.

"No, and it isn't my decision either. But Bill Kenerly and I have had several lengthy conversations about the case and specifically about prosecuting Underwood for the murder of

Catherine Miller, and I have to respect him for soliciting my estimations on the matter, as well as Jerry's."

Gerald "Jerry" Wilson was the Assistant District Attorney who co-prosecuted our case. I had worked more closely with Jerry than any of the other prosecutors in the 24th Judicial District. But Jerry was not feeling well. I worried about his overall health at times as I had observed him chain-smoking, eating unbalanced "meals" of coffee and snack cakes at his desk while he worked, and more and more frequently complaining of headaches. I hoped whatever he had come down with was nothing serious. In any case, I was not going to bother him. He deserved a rest after the four-week trial, on top of everything else he had pending in Superior Court. He and Tom both did, for that matter.

"Of course," I responded to Tom.

"You certainly have done a tremendous job investigating the case, as have the investigators from Rowan County, and you are all to be commended on your efforts. I'm sure Bill would welcome your input, Paula, but I feel fairly certain that he has made up his mind at this juncture," Tom commented.

"I understand that. So, after your discussions, weighing all the pros and cons, and I'm sure you were both very thorough, what does it boil down to, Tom? What tipped his decision from 'We are going to try him for the murder of Catherine Miller' when he left here after the trial, to 'We are *not* going to try him,' and being so firm about it?"

"Paula, I think the biggest reason is – well, I believe there are two primary reasons, actually. First of all, although the circumstantial evidence is, in my opinion, substantial and compelling, there is none of the physical evidence that we fortuitously had in Viktor Gunnarsson's murder. The electrical tape, the shoe impression, and, of course, the head hair with the mitochondrial DNA testimony – all of those were quite impactful on the jury in our trial."

"They were."

"But the Catherine Miller case is lacking this type of scientific evidence that today's society has come to expect, what with all the *CSI* and *Forensic Files* types of television programs, as you are well acquainted. Granted, forensic evidence is not required in every case, but the murder weapon was never found – in *either* case. Testimony and documentation could be offered to prove that L. C. Underwood had a..38 caliber handgun *like* the one that fired the shots that killed Catherine Miller, but without Underwood's gun there is no way to prove that his gun was the murder weapon and that it was in his possession at the time."

"…as I'm well aware. But we do have witnesses who can say that they saw L. C. with the .38 within a day or two of her murder."

"Yes, and that is indisputably favorable circumstantial evidence, but those facts still fail to prove that Underwood used that gun to kill Catherine Miller."

"Right. I understand that."

"The Miller crime scene investigators found no physical evidence at the house – no fingerprints and so forth belonging to Underwood, and even if they had, they would not be particularly helpful since he was known to have visited inside her home on a number of previous occasions. There are the witnesses who say a car like Underwood's parked at the Miller residence the evening of the murder, but none who are willing to say with certainty that it was Underwood's car, and none of them took down the license plate."

"All true."

"I know the circumstantial evidence is compelling. Some might even say it is overwhelming. But it is not physical evidence. Furthermore, you understand *double jeopardy,* do you not?"

I did. Tom was referring to the Double Jeopardy Clause spelled out in the Fifth Amendment to the United States Constitution, the same Amendment that guarantees a citizen charged with a crime Due Process of Law, the right to a jury trial, and protection against self-incrimination:

"No person shall be held to answer for a capital, or otherwise infamous crime, unless on a presentment or indictment of a grand jury, except in cases arising in the land or naval forces, or in the militia, when in actual service in time of war or public danger; nor shall any person be subject for the same offense to be twice put in jeopardy of life or limb; nor shall be compelled in any criminal case to be a witness against himself, nor be deprived of life, liberty, or property, without due process of law; nor shall private property be taken for public use, without just compensation" *(Article V, United States Constitution).*

The Double Jeopardy clause is a guaranteed right to all citizens, protecting them from being prosecuted twice for the same crime (with the same victim at the same time). In other words, a man who beat his wife repeatedly in one day and then shot and killed her could be tried for each separate assault he committed upon her but could only be tried once for shooting and killing her.

"Tom, I know that we have only one shot at prosecuting Underwood for killing Catherine Miller."

"Exactly, and it would be a shame for a jury to decide there was reasonable doubt and to find him not guilty, and then perhaps later, when additional evidence turned up, such as the murder weapon, or even a voluntary confession, we would not be able to try him again."

That would be an abysmal state of affairs indeed. I just did not know what additional evidence could be found at this point. Terry, Don, Steve, and I had followed every possible lead.

"Tom, you said there were a couple of reasons. Aside from scientific evidence, what was the other reason?"

"Underwood's appeals. Our trial went well. Granted, the jury did not recommend the death penalty, but they did find him guilty of both First Degree charges. Underwood received two substantial sentences – Life Imprisonment plus forty years consecutive."

"Right.'

"That is no small accomplishment."

"True. It was well prosecuted."

"Thank you, but I was not fishing for compliments; I was merely stating the fact. I believe that any additional objections the defense might raise on appeal in that case will be denied and the convictions and sentences will only be confirmed. However, if Underwood is tried before a jury in the Miller case, essentially a whole new can of worms will be opened. A plethora of possibilities will come into play. If just one error results in his being found not guilty in the Miller case, it could potentially give him grounds for a judge to grant him a new trial in the Gunnarsson case. Or even if he's convicted in the Miller case, a technicality could win him an appeal in both cases. It is an enormous risk, and I believe Bill Kenerly was being judicious in considering such possibilities."

"I get it. Additionally, I suppose that it is a good thing to have the threat of an indictment in the Miller case hanging over his head," I said.

"Absolutely. Were he to be granted release of some time, such as parole, or should he win an appeal in our case, he could be charged in Rowan County for the murder of Catherine Miller and be forced to remain in custody."

"For everyone's sakes, he needs to be kept behind bars."

"Certainly," Tom agreed.

"All things considered; do you believe Kenerly made the right decision?"

"All things considered, yes I do."

"And Jerry?"

"He can tell you himself, but yes, he is also in agreement."

I exhaled. "Alright then. Thank you for your time. And Tom?"

"Yes?"

"You and Jerry both truly did an amazing job. It's too bad you can't do the same in Salisbury, but I appreciate what you did, and what you continue to do," I said, and meant it.

Jerry later told me in his usual no-nonsense manner that investigators would have to find some more evidence before Bill Kenerly would ever indict L. C. Underwood.

"We searched for three and a half years," I reminded him.

"And that's on them, not you. You did your job here."

"I know, but Kay and Jason…"

"I know, but you can't save the world, Paula."

"So I've been told."

"It is not a bad thing that you still strive for justice. Sometimes it's just not realistic."

"So I've learned."

"…and it's a good thing to care about people as you obviously do. You have a heart of gold," he said.

"Yeah, well, so does a hard-boiled egg," I responded.

Jerry chuckled, and then he started coughing.

"I'm glad you're back, Jerry. I hope you're feeling better," I told him.

"Well, good health is overrated. It amounts to the slowest possible rate at which one can die," Jerry said flatly.

"That is not a very optimistic outlook," I pointed out.

"I've been in this business too long to be terribly optimistic," he said.

"Touché."

Jerry picked up a box of Little Debbie snack cakes and offered me one. I shook my head.

"It'll cheer you up," he said.

"I think it might make me feel worse," I said. "Then I'd be a Little Debbie Downer."

He shook his head and grinned. Then he pulled open the plastic wrap and bit off a good portion of a raisin cream pie.

As I walked across the street to my office, I considered the facts. Tom Rusher, Jerry Wilson, and Don concurred with District Attorney Kenerly. While I also understood the arguments, I could not help but be disappointed that L. C. would not face a jury trial for murdering Catherine Miller. I knew I would be holding my breath as soon as Underwood started filing appeals. There would be enough to deal with concerning L. C. Underwood still to come. In the meantime, I would move on to the next horrific cases of human depravity to which I had been assigned and try to help those I could along the way.

I feared that Kay, on the other hand, would be devastated and possibly feel victimized all over again. She had already lost so much, and although L. C. was behind bars, Kay needed all the support she could get. She needed hope for the future and justice in some form for her mother's murder. I could not presently give her much hope of the latter. I loved my profession, but sometimes it felt as if I were accomplishing little to nothing at all.

Kay was livid.

"I will NEVER accept this decision. Not ever!" she exclaimed.

"Kay, I don't know what to say. I'm sorry, Kay. I am so sorry," I told her. I felt like the four of us had let her down.

"Don told me that I was going to have to find a way to accept it. I can't. I won't!" she said.

"How did you find out, Kay?" I asked. "Did Bill Kenerly call you?"

"Hah! No, he did not call me! Of all the chicken sh*t things, I had to find out in a letter from him in the mail!"

"Are you serious?" I asked.

"Yes. The letter came in the mail. I opened the mailbox, and there it was. I read it right then and there. And you know what? If I had been a balloon, I would have just deflated down to nothing right then and there. I could not believe Kenerly went back on his word."

"Did you call him then?" I asked her.

"No. I was so mad; I did not want to talk to him at that point. I called Don instead. That's when Don told me that

I would just have to accept Kenerly's decision. You know how Don is, in his agent voice, without emotion, just matter of fact. That didn't sit well with me either."

Maybe I should have offered to tell her. But it wasn't my place; it was their case.

"Don tried to explain that it would be to my benefit to try and be happy that L. C. was in prison for Viktor's murder and may never get out of prison."

"Right. Are you going to talk to Bill Kenerly?" I persisted.

"I don't know. I really don't think so. I am *so mad!* It would not be a good thing for us to be in the same room together. My mother and I both supported him when he was running for D.A., and I am so disappointed that he did not at least meet with me face to face and try to explain his decision. I would at least have respected him for that."

"How is Jason? Did you tell him?"

"I *can't* tell him, Paula, at least not now. I have to find a way to process this. Jason has been through enough already without adding this to him. It isn't going to make a difference, and it will only make Jason angrier. He's barely speaking to me anyway. And to find out his grandmother…" Kay's voice broke then, and she began to cry. "…It will hurt Jason. I'm not going to tell him right now."

I wanted to cry too, but I didn't.

"You know one of the things that hurts me the most?" Kay asked me as she wiped the remains of her mascara from her tear troughs.

"What's that?"

"Bill Kenerly is a member of my church. He goes to my church – mine and my mother's church – where my mother has served for so many years! Yet he did not have the decency to tell me himself that he had decided not to prosecute L. C. for murdering my mother in cold blood. He either just doesn't want to bother or he's a coward! Either way, I am so angry at him!"

Who was I to argue when her pain was so severe, her nerves so raw, her anger so tangible? It was not my place. I did, however, pray one of many prayers that God would bring her peace one day, and healing. I spoke with Kay frequently after that conversation, and as time went on, it was clear to me that Kay was not coping well. She did not seem to be healing as I had expected. If anything, she seemed more stressed with each passing month. I could tell from our conversations that she was withdrawing more and more from her community, and I sensed that her circle of friends was getting smaller. Worst of all was the fact that Jason was still angry with Kay, still blaming her for Catherine's murder and all the other terrible things that L. C. Underwood had wrought upon their lives. That fact, above all else, was breaking Kay's heart all over again.

"Kay, there's something I want to say to you," I told her.

"What is it?"

"I don't know why you are having to go through all the things you are going through. But you just have to go on living. You have to keep hanging in there, and you can because you are a survivor; I know you are. It won't be for naught. One day, I genuinely believe that one day, you will be someone else's survival guide. You may become a walking, talking survival guide for a lot of hurting, suffering people."

"I don't see how," she said.

"In time you will."

CHAPTER SEVEN

**"All they that know thee among the
people shall be astonished at thee:
thou shalt be a terror, and never shalt
thou be any more." (Ezekiel 28:19)**

Kay's fears of L. C. getting released from prison or escaping seemed to be intensifying. Each time he was moved from one location to another, for administrative purposes or whatever the reason, Kay would call me, Don, Terry, and sometimes all four of us. It seemed that after the trial, Kay found herself going over every detail, not only of the trial, but of her entire relationship with L. C., and it took months, nay even years, for Kay to put events in their proper order and magnitude. Processing all that had happened in and out of her presence overwhelmed her at times, and with good reason. All of it exacerbated her fear of L. C.

My husband, Randy, a Probation Supervisor with the North Carolina Department of Corrections, had some degree of access to L. C.'s prison record, and Kay was always asking me to have him find out what was going on with L. C. Was L. C. in general population? Would he be considered for work release? Why was he being moved to a less secure facility when he had been convicted of First Degree Murder? She was absolutely terrified that he would get out without her knowledge, and to be perfectly candid, I shared her fears, though perhaps not always to the same degree of intensity. L. C. Underwood was dangerous and unpredictable.

I recalled the night the four of us – Don, Terry, Steve, and I – were conducting surveillance at the home of Beth Richardson, a woman L. C. had met and become romantically involved with shortly before he was arrested, despite the fact that he never did completely cease his stalking of Kay Weden. We discovered the new girlfriend, Beth, through reviewing L. C.'s phone records from a trap and trace device, one of the seemingly endless endeavors we attempted while searching for new evidence. We received copies of the list of all of L. C.'s incoming and outgoing calls for several months. For a couple of months, L. C. made lengthy calls to, and received lengthy calls from, Beth's home phone. We decided it was time to pay her a visit.

Don made the initial contact with Beth, who promptly kicked him out of her condo with finality. L. C. anticipated that we would eventually find out about her and try to warn her about him, and he was correct. L. C., in a preemptory tactic, told Beth that he had been accused of a crime he did not commit because Don Gale, of whom he painted a devious picture, supposedly had a personal problem with him and was trying to get him fired from the Salisbury Police Department. Beth had no reason at that point to doubt what L. C. told her, but after Don's brief initial visit, she wisely began to ask herself some questions that had been nagging her. As I had predicted, it did not take Beth more than a few days until she reached out to Don, and he and I went together to talk with her at her parents' home. The ugly truth dawned on her as we provided her with the facts, and her family was understandably flummoxed.

The lies L. C. had told Beth were predictable yet outrageous. He told her that he had married for the first and only time at the age of thirty, and that he and his wife had divorced amicably after ten years. He told her that Jason Weden had broken into his house and stolen a gun.

He told her that Jason was also the prime suspect in his grandmother's murder, that he had robbed her, shot her, and then trashed the house to make it look like a gang of robbers had invaded her house. L. C. told her that the Swedish man found murdered in Watauga County was killed by Swedish hitmen, and he adamantly denied *ever* having been to the mountains of North Carolina.

When Beth tried to end the relationship and terminate contact with L. C., he was outraged. As with Kay, he alternated between begging her to give him another chance and threatening her. He stalked her relentlessly. I worried about her in particular because, like me, she had a young daughter, Gail, living with her. My worries came to fruition one day when Beth made an urgent phone call to Don. Of the four of us, Don lived in closest proximity to Beth and Gail.

"Beth, what's going on?" Don asked her, sensing that something that amiss.

"I got home from work today, as usual, about ten minutes after six. My usual habit – which L. C. well knew – was to unlock the kitchen door, walk in, and light a cigarette."

"And is that what you did today?" Don asked her.

"No, thank the Lord! I don't know why, but I didn't immediately light up a cigarette. I, I saw that the gas burner on my kitchen stove was on! My apartment was full of gas!"

"Had *you* left the gas on?" Don asked.

"No! I hadn't even used the stove in two days!" Beth realized that someone had entered her apartment – with a key – and turned on the gas. She had a fairly good idea of who it was, as did the four of us.

"Will you let Paula know what happened as well?" Beth asked.

"She's with me now. I'll tell her," Don said.

"Thank you."

We were all concerned about Beth's safety. We decided to provide around-the-clock surveillance at her residence, hoping that if we could catch L. C. trespassing or attempting something even worse, we could take him into custody. Beth asked if I would stay close to her, and empathetic with her fear, I agreed.

I spoke with Sheriff Lyons by phone to let him know what was going on.

"I know she'll be glad to have you there with her, but please be safe," he said.

"Always."

I packed enough clothing for a few days, ensured that Randy was available to take care of Katie, and drove to Charlotte.

Beginning on that hot Friday evening in August of 1995, Don and I stayed inside the residence with Beth while others surveilled and patrolled her neighborhood. She was visibly shaken. That night, L. C. called Beth repeatedly. I could hear the desperation in his voice growing with each subsequent call. In addition to all the voicemail messages he left her, there were a number of hang up calls from an "unknown number" as well. Beth paced. I told her to go to bed and let us keep watch for her, but she said it would be impossible. She dozed a bit on the sofa. I slept for a few hours the next day, but that evening, which was a Saturday, Don and I stayed up together inside Beth's condo to keep watch. Don, Terry, Steve, Beth, and I all had the same feeling that L. C. was going to do something.

L. C. was becoming noticeably more desperate with each phone call he attempted, each voicemail he left. We did not have to wait long that night. Just before 1:00 AM on Sunday morning, L. C. showed up. He drove into her condominium complex and headed directly for her building, although he approached it slowly. An agent outside watched as he stretched his neck to check out all of the cars in the parking lot. The agent reported each move he made to us on an confidential, encrypted channel on a police radio.

The agent informed us that L. C. had inadvertently spotted an unmarked police car in the parking lot. He quickly turned around and drove toward the street. Instead of pulling out immediately, he paused, put the car into reverse and commenced to back up, as if he had changed his mind and was coming back. Again, however, he stopped and changed course. He pulled out into the street this time and drove slowly away.

Ten minutes later, Beth received another hang-up call. Don instructed Beth to answer the phone, but the caller hung up as soon as she answered. At 4:30 AM, another officer confirmed that L. C. was back at home, with both of his vehicles parked in the driveway. We maintained security and surveillance at Beth's apartment for a few more days until the stress nearly got the better of her.

"I don't know how long I can take this," Beth confided in me when we were standing in her bedroom. "My nerves are on edge, and I am just sick with worry. I can't believe I got caught up with someone like him. I'm afraid, Paula, and I don't really know how to deal with it. I've never felt this kind of fear before, worrying about him showing up everywhere I go…"

"I do know, Beth, and I am so sorry. It's so stressful being afraid." A Roman philosopher by the name of Seneca the Younger described the fearful in the following: "They lose the day in expectation of the night, and the night in fear of the dawn." He could have been describing Beth only a couple thousand years in the future, give or take a couple of years.

"It's like a bad dream I can't wake from… except I can't sleep."

I nodded.

"I really wish y'all could just go ahead and arrest him. I think it's the only way I will truly feel safe."

"So do I, Beth. So do I."

"Until you do, I have decided to take my daughter and move back in with my parents," Beth said.

"I was hoping you would do that," I told her. "You will never be able to relax here. Your parents will be glad for you to be there with them."

"They are. They are worried about me, and now that I know the truth about Kay's mother, I can't help but worry about my own parents. I'd rather be there with them."

"That sounds like a smart move to me."

"I don't feel very smart. I fell for his lies," she said, looking both embarrassed and tired.

"Trusting someone doesn't make you less smart. Taking advantage of someone's trust and good nature, like L. C. did, is beyond wrong. You aren't the only person he ever fooled, but we would like to stop him from sucking anyone else into his dangerous web of lies. But we can only do so much."

"God help the next woman that gets tangled up with that man," Beth said. Indeed.

"Perhaps his next girlfriend will be Guido or Bubba …in general population."

Beth smiled at that, the first smile I had seen from her in days. She seemed more relaxed once she made up her mind to move Gail and herself back in with her parents.

"You know that old saying, Paula, about you don't know what you have until it's gone?"

"Sure."

"Well, I know now what I had, and I'm *glad* he's gone! I just hope he will stay gone for good."

Don kept in touch with Beth, who continued to receive calls from L. C., even at her parents' home, though not with the same intensity or frequency that she had while living in her condo. I was so incredibly thankful, however, that the next time Beth laid her eyes on L.C Underwood was when she saw his mug on the news broadcast announcing his arrest for the murder of Viktor Gunnarsson. She and her daughter were safe, assuming we could keep L. C. in custody.

I had been afraid for Beth and for Kay both, but I was also afraid for myself. L. C. had proven that he had no limitations, no boundaries when he tried to kill Beth in a natural gas explosion, someone he claimed to love, as well as her young daughter. He certainly would have no qualms about killing me, given the opportunity. He would, I was convinced, take immense pleasure in the act.

Sometime after L. C.'s conviction and sentencing, I was at my desk in the Sheriff's Office when my phone buzzed. It was Patricia Shook, or "Trish," as we called her, one of our most outstanding dispatchers in our 911 Communications Center.

"There's someone on the line from the state Attorney General's Office," Trish told me. "I think it's the Attorney General himself if I understood correctly."

"Okay, I'll take it, thank you," I said and pressed the line with the flashing light.

"Hello. This is Detective Sergeant May," I said.

"Paula May?" he asked, for clarification.

"Yes, sir, it is."

"You were the lead investigator in the homicide case for which Lamont Claxton Underwood is currently serving time?"

"Yes, sir."

"Well, I have something in my hand right now, and I wanted to be the one to tell you about it directly. I wanted to make sure for my own peace of mind that you knew about it."

"Alright, I appreciate that. But what is it?"

"It's a handwritten note. Well, shall I say it's a letter of sorts, but it is 101 pages, handwritten by Underwood on a lined, yellow legal pad."

"About the case? About me?"

"It's about you specifically," he said.

"I'm listening," I replied.

"It's not pleasant," he warned me.

"I am already aware, sir, that he is not president of my fan club."

"Of course," he said. "I just wanted to give you fair warning."

"I understand."

"He is fairly clear that he wants to see you dead. Perhaps it is all just fantasy, but he does write wanting to see your head basically shot into and your blood exploded all over the place," as I recall.

"Like Catherine Miller."

"Pardon?"

"That sounds like the Catherine Miller crime scene. We are confident he murdered her, but the D.A. in Salisbury doesn't feel like there's enough to prosecute him there. A lot of circumstantial evidence. She was found murdered in the kitchen of her home, shot twice in the head. There was a burst of blood spatter on the refrigerator."

"That's... interesting, in light of what he wrote about *you*. He seems to be, for lack of a better word, obsessed with the notion. He has clearly given it a great deal of thought, not that there is a lot of other things for him to do in there but think. I just – I am concerned that he is hyper-focused on you."

"I can't say I'm particularly surprised, sir. When he gets something on his mind, he can't let it go. He stalked and terrorized his ex-fiancé Kay Weden for months. But deep inside, he hates women, and it was just his bad luck – or mine I guess – that I was assigned Viktor Gunnarsson's murder case. I am thankful that he is in prison now."

"It sounds like he's right where he needs to be. But he does seem fairly confident that he is going to win his next appeal. Perhaps he is being delusional, I don't know. But in the event that he does not win an appeal, he has tried to enlist another inmate to help him escape, and possibly to help him get the job done. We are investigating that now." The hair on the back of my neck rose. Sure, I had been threatened before, by other violent offenders, but it had never affected me the way that L. C.'s threats had. And Kay! Kay would be terrified if she knew for a fact that L. C. was thinking in these terms. She was undoubtedly high on his list as well, as was her son Jason.

"Sir, did you say 101 pages?"

"Yes, 51 pages, front and back. It appears to be a journal, an elaborate plan of sorts."

"How does he imagine killing me?" I asked, not sure I wanted to hear the answer. "Does he say?"

"There are multiple methods listed. None of them are pleasant. Most of them would… take place slowly, painfully. And he's talking with another inmate, a third man, about possible payment to do it for him if he does not get out. But he's also planning an escape if his next appeal fails, or at least he was."

"How did you come into possession of the letter?" I asked.

"Guards found it in a shake."

"They shook down only L. C.'s cell?"

"No, the entire block. A random shake. But then we interviewed one of the other inmates, and he was cooperative. Said he had no intentions of hurting anyone or taking anyone's money. He thinks Underwood is just running his mouth, but…"

"But there's no way to be certain."

"Correct. We just wanted you to know. I personally wanted to make sure you knew."

"Thank you for telling me. Sir, I'd like a copy of the letter."

"No problem; I will make sure you get one. We're hanging on to the original."

"What will happen to him now? How much trouble is he in?"

"Well, frankly I don't know that we have enough to charge him criminally. The information was forwarded over to us from Central Prison. This letter – this *writing* – just states what he'd *like* to do to you. There's enough probably to cite him on an offense internally for conspiring to escape. But to be honest, that's really about it at this point. It will, however, keep him in solitary for a while, and it will come up every time he attempts to go before the Parole Board."

I was trying to take notes about everything he said, as he was telling me.

"I see that he was convicted in Watauga County for First Degree Kidnapping and First Degree Murder on July 25, 1997, and that he is serving a Life sentence, plus forty years for the kidnapping."

"Yes, it's to be served consecutively, not concurrently."

"I see that also. Detective Sergeant May, are you on the SAVAN network, to get updates on his movements?"

"Yes."

"Good. Stay on it. Make sure you're active, that you're on the system at all times."

"I am, and I will. In fact, every time he is moved, I generally hear about it first from Kay Weden, the girlfriend of the man he murdered up here. She is really afraid he will get out, and frankly, she has good reason to be afraid, in my opinion."

"Well, right now it seems he is blaming you for his current plight, which is a direct result of the Gunnarsson homicide…"

"…which is a direct result of his own actions, not mine. I just investigated the case, along with three others on my team."

"Of course. The three others – they were males, I presume?"

"Yes, sir."

"I know you know him probably better than I. But his prison record shows him to have a narcissistic personality with extreme fears of abandonment that may stem from his mother primarily?"

"Yes, at least that is what I understand to be a significant area of emotional trauma for him. He was abandoned by both parents, but he seems hyper-focused on his mother. He has serious relationship issues, but where females are concerned, he is... despicable, to say the least."

"Yes, and it says…with an extreme propensity for violence. This is why I want you to be aware that you have – in particular – been on his mind."

"And not in a good way," I interpreted.

"No, I'm afraid not."

"I appreciate the call. Will you inform me if you or someone in your office decides to prosecute him for the threats against me or the escape or anything?"

"We are reviewing the case now, and yes, we certainly will be in touch. We will require your cooperation if that turns out to be the case."

"Yes, sir, I understand."

"You have my number in the meantime in case you need anything."

"I made a note of it. Thank you for taking the time to call me personally."

"Yes, ma'am. Try to have a good day."

"You too, Sir."

I informed my supervisor, Lieutenant Allen Stout, who was standing in the back door frame smoking a cigarette.

"101 pages! That man's nutty as a squirrel turd."

"And he's more mean than crazy."

"Yeah. He's proven that he's dangerous. I've had my share of threats, and I know it can eat at you," Lieutenant Stout said to me. "But mostly they're all talk – bullies – and wouldn't do anything if they had the chance." I knew he was trying to make me feel better.

"Yeah, most of them. But there always has to be that one…" I countered.

"Well, you just gotta be ready to take care of business if that happens," he advised. "In the meantime, we probably ought to make the sheriff aware." He took one more draw on the cigarette, tossed it on the ground, and smeared it out with his shoe.

Lieutenant Stout had been in law enforcement longer than I, and like all of us, had received his share of threats. He did not seem to let many things bother him, although his blood pressure had crept up to the point that he now required medication for it. On the outside, he seemed to take things in stride. But there were times he seemed troubled to me, like something was bothering him. When I asked, however, he consistently said that "everything was hunky-dory." I did not press him.

Kim Scott, Sheriff Lyons' Administrative Assistant, walked in with a file for me.

"Are you okay?" Kim asked, looking at me closely. We graduated from high school together, but I never really got to know her until she was hired in 1989, about the same time that I became a detective.

"Yeah, I'm fine," I assured her.

"Are you sure? You look like something's wrong," she said.

"Let's go get some lunch," I suggested, "and I'll tell you all about it." Kim had become a really good friend. She was outgoing, hilariously funny, and just beautiful with her fabulous, dimpled smile. Everyone warmed to her right away. Her company was just what I needed; she always made me feel better. I told her about L. C.'s threats.

"That vile man isn't ever gonna give you any peace, is he?" she remarked when I told her about L. C.'s writings, his threats.

"Doesn't look like it," I agreed.

"Well, he doesn't know who he's messing with then."

"You'd think he would have a pretty good idea by now," I said.

"Apparently not if he thinks he's gonna get away with an escape plan and threatening you. Have you told Randy yet?" she asked.

"Not yet. I'll tell him tonight."

"One good thing about it is that L. C.'d be out of your life in no time if he tried to carry out his threats."

"How's that?" I asked.

"He'd be history. That would be a suicide mission for him if he came anywhere around you or the Sheriff's Office. So maybe you should look on the bright side, stop worrying about what could go wrong, and think about what could go right, if he ever tries anything."

Kim certainly had a unique and positive outlook.

"If I know Randy, he'd kill L. C. in a heartbeat if he ever caught him around your house, or you or Katie...that is, if you didn't see him first," she added.

"Yeah...if we saw him coming."

"He'd be so full of lead it would take a bulldozer to move him."

"Probably so," I agreed. Kim made me feel better already.

"Let's order dessert," I suggested.

When I got home that evening, I told Randy about L. C.'s threats.

"He's not gonna get out, Paula, and definitely not anytime soon. Plus, he doesn't have the money to hire somebody else to do something, especially to a woman cop."

"You can't know that, and besides, he does have enough money. He has plenty."

"Well, if I ever see him come anywhere around here, he'll wish he'd never been born. I'm not gonna stand around and see what he's gonna do. He's already said what he wants to do, so if he ever comes around you, you have reason to protect yourself, and so do I."

"That's just it, Randy. He wouldn't do that. He would hide. He would watch for us at a distance. We'd never see it coming."

"That's not his M.O. It wasn't on either of his other homicides. He shot Viktor Gunnarsson and Catherine Miller at close range, face to face."

"That's true, but he's had a lot of time to think about things now. He's had time to plan better. Plus, he's probably gotten himself a good criminal education since he's been locked up."

"Paula, we'll be the first to know if he escapes or gets released."

"I hope so," I said doubtfully.

"It doesn't do any good to worry," he said, and of course he was right in that it accomplished nothing. Besides, I didn't worry all the time. But when it was on my mind, the possibilities seemed endless. My imagination ran freely and unleashed.

The seed of fear had already been planted, watered, and fertilized. I rubbed my sweaty palms on my pants and tried to think of something – anything – else. Because of the new information, however, the confirmation that I, specifically, was on L. C.'s mind, I experienced a fear that never left me entirely, but which reared its ugly head when it was least expected, and which robbed me of the peace of mind I should have had.

I was a Christian, saved by grace through faith in the Lord Jesus Christ and his work of redemption. I was going to Heaven when I died, whenever that might be, not because of any good that I had done but because I had accepted the free gift of salvation. Then what was there to fear, really, when death amounted to only the entrance into Heaven, to spend eternity in a beautiful place where sin, murder, violence, and all forms of evil were never present? For now, though, I resided in my humanity, and my mortal flesh wanted to live.

I wanted to be present to raise my daughter. Katie was my joy, my life. I did not want her to grow up without her mother, and God forbid that some monster like L. C. Underwood ever tried to do anything to hurt her. Without hesitation, I would claw his eyeballs out with my fingernails if he ever so much as came near her. At times, my vivid and creative imagination seemed more like a curse, and that line of thinking was only exacerbating my fear. I was angry that a man like L. C. Underwood had to occupy my thoughts. I deliberately called to mind what Sheriff Lyons had said. I determined to cling to my faith and to God's protection.

I also remembered something Sgt. Joe Moody once told a woman when we both responded to a domestic violence call. The woman lived in constant fear of her husband. He had beaten her down both physically and mentally to the point that she was afraid to leave, afraid to move. I never wanted to let fear control me like that.

"There comes a time," Sergeant Moody told her, "when you have to take the fear that paralyzes you and turn it around. Let that same fear motivate you instead." It was good advice for any number of situations.

There were times, however, when I was caught off guard, or when fear would creep in gradually. At other times, it would rise suddenly from somewhere deep inside. I could taste it. It rose in my throat like bile. At other times still, it would reach down my throat, into my chest and squeeze my heart and lungs until I felt as if I could not breathe. It seemed to be a living, breathing thing with which I had to battle persistently.

Only a few weeks had passed after I got the call from the Attorney General's Office that I sat straight up in bed, startled from a deep sleep. Randy was working late, checking on his probation clients. Katie was asleep in her room.

I lay still for a few minutes, waiting to see if I heard anything else. Then I recognized the unmistakable sound of twigs popping, as if someone or something was stepping on fallen tree limbs. The front of our two-story colonial was all grassy lawn, but the back was situated along a wood line. As quietly as I could, I got up, grabbed my shoes from the closet and the 12-gauge. I was not going to mess around with a pistol.

After peeking in on Katie, I slipped quietly down the stairs in the dark to the main level of the house. I slid my feet into my shoes and unlocked the kitchen door leading into the garage. I resisted the urge to flip on the lights. The side door leading outside was still locked. I opened it as quietly as I could, but the rubber seal on the bottom of the door made a swishing sound as it scraped the concrete floor. It was not completely dark with a streetlight from the church parking lot on the hill near our house, but it was dark enough. As I stepped outside, I heard the sound of feet tromping through the woods above me. I racked a shell into the shotgun.

"Hold it right there!" I called out to whoever or whatever was there. I heard the crackling of leaves but could not see anything. I heard rapid footsteps, and they were moving further away. I should have grabbed a flashlight as I came outside, but my hands had been occupied carrying my shoes and the shotgun. Now both hands were firmly gripping the shotgun as I headed up the hill and into the woods. I stopped at a large pin oak at the tree line and listened. Silence. I leaned against the oak tree and waited. I would stay there as long as necessary, in my nightgown and the cold mountain air. I leaned against the old tree and listened, but I only heard the wind. After about twenty minutes of shivering, not hearing another sound, I changed my mind and went back inside.

"Mama?" Katie called out, as I started back up the stairs. "Mama, where are you?"

"I'm coming, Katiebug." I walked into her bedroom and saw that she was sitting up in the middle of the bed, her long spindly legs curled beneath her. Gymnastics classes had made her natural flexibility even more flexible.

"Mama, where were you?" she asked, worriedly.

"I had to go outside just for a minute. What's the matter?" I asked her.

"I had a bad dream," she said.

I picked her up and held her for a minute, then I slid us both under her fluffy down comforter and held her close.

"What did you dream about?" I whispered.

"Some man was trying to get me," she said groggily.

"No one's ever gonna get you," I promised. "Jesus will take care of all of us." I prayed it would be so.

CHAPTER EIGHT

**"My heart is sore pained within me: and the
terrors of death are fallen upon me."
(Psalm 55:4)**

I could not deny that the phone call from the Attorney General's Office made me uneasy, and the possibility of a prowler around my house, a trespasser at my home, only heightened my anxiety. I checked out a pair of night vision goggles from the supply room at the sheriff's office so that the next time I heard something or someone outside my home I would have some visibility in the dark without having to silhouette myself with a flashlight. I was afraid of the possibilities, but more so than fear, I felt anger. A home is supposed to be a place of refuge, a place to feel safe, sheltered, protected, and now it wasn't.

There were other nights when I was convinced someone was outside our home, but neither Randy nor I was ever able to see anyone. At other times when I was working late and driving home after dark, I wondered if I was being followed. I could not pinpoint anyone or anything in particular, but I had a strong feeling that someone was watching me. I told myself I was being ridiculous. Still, I made sure I was armed off duty as well as on duty, and I was careful not to maintain the same routes and routines every day. I was on hyper-alert. At times I was more diligent and alert than at others, but as weeks passed and then months, my fears were not realized; I began to relax.

Kay, on the other hand, seemed somewhat lost, and her anxiety was more intense and longer lasting. We had worked so hard so that, among other desirable outcomes, Kay could have peace. Even with L. C. in prison, Kay was decidedly *not* at peace. When she called me, the pain in her voice was obvious.

"I am terrified L. C. is planning some kind of revenge," she admitted to me one evening when she called. I wanted to reassure her, but I could not give her any guarantees.

"I worry about him too, Kay, but we cannot live our lives in fear. It is crippling."

"And it's even more than that," she said. "It's the people around me. People I thought were my friends."

"What do you mean?" I asked.

"Well, everyone avoids me like the plague," she told me.

"Who avoids you?" I asked.

"Everyone I know. It's like I have two heads or something. Everything that L. C. did to me has been in the newspapers, on TV, on the radio, and people I have known for years now just pretend like they don't see me when we pass on the street or in the grocery store."

"Kay, don't you think it is much more likely that people simply do not know what to say, how to express their condolences, their sympathy? People are not generally equipped to deal with the kind of tragedy you and Jason have had to endure, the violence in particular. They would rather stick their heads in the sand sometimes, you know, trying to pretend that kind of thing doesn't really happen."

"And that's another thing," she told me. "It's one thing to treat me like a stranger. But they treat Jason the same way."

"What do you mean, Kay? What has been going on?" I asked.

"Well, I know Jason is still really angry. He takes a lot of his anger out on me. I know he blames me for bringing L. C. into our lives and killing his grandmother, and I know he has a point, even though it is driving us apart. But Jason has always had his friends, you know, like his soccer teammates and friends from school."

"Right. You said they were always hanging around your house, eating your food and so on."

"Yes. They did. They don't so much anymore."

"But why?"

"It's like the other evening when Jason had a friend over. He told us that his mother did not like him being there; she did not want him at my house, and she doesn't want Jason at hers. That really hurt me because I thought his mother, Sue, was my friend. It hurt me even more because what she said also hurt Jason."

"But why did she say that? Did you ask her?"

"I did ask her, and she didn't deny it. But she said that she did not feel like her son was safe with us because she did not understand the things that were happening, or had happened, and that someone may still be after us!"

"But that is ridiculous! L. C. is in prison."

"I know, and I told her that, but it didn't seem to matter. Sue is not the only one. In fact, I heard that some of the boys' mothers had talked with each other about it. They are nice to my face, but behind my back they are talking about us like we are some sort of freaks or something. They want to keep their distance from us."

"I see. I'm sorry. People can be insensitive. Sometimes they speak before they think."

"I know. Like right after we buried my mother, when I returned to teaching, one of the coaches, whom I considered a friend, was walking me down the hallway of the high school. Instead of asking how Jason and I were doing or saying he was sorry for our loss, he asked me if I was afraid *for the students*. I told him no, that I had no reason to be. Then he asked me if I weren't afraid that L. C. or one of his buddies could be hiding in the woods behind the school to 'blow me away' one day as I went to and from my car. Comments like that do not help my already shattered nerves."

"I'm sure they don't. Kay, people just – they don't understand, and they probably have no idea how hurtful their actions are."

"But who does that? Who tells a young boy that has lost his last grandparent that he is no longer welcome in their home?"

"I don't know. They clearly weren't thinking about anyone other than themselves."

"Maybe. They think Jason and I are mixed up in something bad. They don't understand, and they don't want to get involved. All they know is what they read in the newspaper. They don't want to get near us!"

"They are only thinking of themselves and their family members, trying to be protective I guess."

"I suppose. But Jason has been through so much already."

"I know, Kay, and so have you."

"I don't think I can stay in Salisbury."

"I wondered about that," I told her.

"I don't even want to go to church because I don't know what I will do if I see Bill Kenerly there."

"Well, he's the one that ought to be uncomfortable around you, not vice versa."

"I still can't believe Bill never called me. I just want to leave this town."

"I understand. So, where would you go?"

"I'm not sure yet. I just don't feel safe here anymore. I don't feel like Jason and I belong here anymore, especially with my mother gone."

"I'm sure you have a lot of memories there."

"I have some good memories here. But I have some horrible memories here too. Things I need to move past somehow."

"I can't imagine how difficult it has been for you and Jason."

"There are so many places I can't go near. I can't even drive past them."

"Like what kind of places?" I asked.

"Well, my mother's house of course. She is on the other end of our development, but you know, I can't even look in that direction."

"I certainly understand that."

"But not just there. My mother's office, where she worked all those years."

"She rarely missed a day of work, I remember, for more than forty years!"

"Right. And certain restaurants, and even the church. Too many bad memories are associated with those places."

Nearly five years had passed since her mother was murdered, nearly a year after L. C. was convicted of murdering Viktor Gunnarsson, but for Kay not much had changed.

"Terry Agner advised me to stay put until L. C. was convicted. He wanted to make sure I was safe. He told me people knew me here and I would be safer than going somewhere else where no one knew me."

"That makes sense," I told her. "But now L. C. is behind bars, and you and Jason are safe." I did not sound convincing even to my own ears. "If you want to move, though, then you have to do what your heart tells you. If you feel that you need to go, then I encourage you to go."

"What if he gets out?" she asked, her voice trembling.

"He won't," I said firmly.

"But what if he does?" I could not even guarantee my own safety, much less hers.

"We'll know immediately if that happens." At least I hoped we would.

"You will tell me if you hear anything like that, right? You will tell me right away."

"You know I will. But you are safe now. You and Jason are both safe."

"I don't think I will ever feel safe again," she said sadly.

I felt so sorry for Kay and Jason. It all seemed so unfair. Kay just kept getting victimized with every turn. But I understood her fear, and although I did not want to encourage it, I shared it. I had no doubt that L. C. would come after both of us with vengeance. He saw his current plight not as a consequence of his own actions, but as a direct result of ours – and mine, specifically.

After L. C. had spent a few months in Central Prison in Raleigh, they moved him from maximum to a medium security facility in the eastern part of the state, near the coast. Kay called me shortly afterward with news.

"There's an article in the *Salisbury Post* about L. C. in prison. He was apparently involved with helping other inmates earn their G.E.D. Can you believe that?"

"Frankly, no." I did not want to explain Gain Time to Kay, but I suspected that was what L. C. was trying to do, to take some time off his forty-year sentence.

"I guess he got bored, maybe."

Ironically, it was that very news article that reminded everyone that he was a former cop. Word got back to the prison inmates who were also featured in the article. L. C. had lied to them about what he did for a living, not that I could blame him for choosing not to disclose the fact that he was a police officer. Yet somehow, they had found out, and word spread quickly through the prison. L. C. was panicking. Feeling that his life was in danger, he petitioned the Department of Corrections to transfer him for safety reasons.

Sometime after that, they moved L. C. back to the center of the state, still in a medium security facility, but much closer to Salisbury. Kay and I were both uneasy about that. It was the summer of 1998, and Jason had just been accepted for enrollment at Western Carolina University in Cullowhee. Kay had sold her house and was ready to leave Salisbury.

"I've been accepted into grad school," she told me by phone.

"Good for you, Kay! That is wonderful! Go for it!" I was so pleased that Kay was moving forward to a brighter future. I heard true hope and optimism in her voice for the first time.

"Are you resigning from West Rowan High then?" I asked.

"No, they are actually allowing me to take a one-year's sabbatical leave. This way I won't lose my benefits and so on. After that I will decide, but to be honest, I think they believe, as do I, that I won't be back."

"Let me guess where you will be going to grad school... Western?"

"Yes! I will be in grad school there while Jason earns his degree. I've found a house that I absolutely love, and I've put an offer on it. It's like a mountain retreat with lots of windows on top of a mountain, and I have an amazing view. No one can get to me without me seeing them coming for at least a mile away!"

"It sounds wonderful! Is it far from town then?"

"Not too far, but the road is something else. I mean, there's all kinds of switchbacks, and you really have to know where you are going to find my house, my neighborhood. It's called Frady Cove, and there are only seven houses in it. My house has a large deck, and when it's clear, guess what I can see right from my living room?"

"What?" I asked, excited for her.

"That huge cross over at Balsam!"

I was familiar with the cross to which she referred. It was erected in memory of a

15-year-old girl by the name of Lyn Lowry who died of leukemia in 1962. Lyn loved to vacation in the mountains of western North Carolina, and upon her passing, her parents selected the location to build a permanent memorial to her. The cross stands at a height of sixty feet and is illuminated at night. It can be seen from as far as thirty miles away if the sky is clear. The Reverend Billy Graham led the dedication ceremony with words of peace and hope. I prayed that it would serve as a symbol of peace and hope to Kay as well.

In the months that followed, I did not hear from Kay quite as frequently. When we did talk, she sounded as if she had truly found a home where she was at ease, with moments of contentment if not actual happiness. She completed her master's degree, and Western Carolina University offered her a position teaching as an adjunct instructor right away. It was not long until she was also teaching as an adjunct at Southwestern Community College as well. She was staying busy, doing the thing she loved most: teaching.

Jason lived with Kay off and on during that time, sometimes staying on campus at Western, and sometimes commuting from Kay's mountain home. Yet there was still a seemingly impenetrable barrier between them, solidified with the mortar of anger, blame, and resentment. They shared a living space; they shared meals. Occasionally they watched television shows together. But nothing Kay could do or say seemed to reach Jason or melt the anger he held inside.

Jason had suffered the loss of friends, almost everyone with whom he had attended high school, and his precious grandmother, Catherine. Jason had also suffered embarrassment by having his mother's personal life – and vicariously his – spread all over the news media for everyone he knew to see, to gape at, to intrude upon. It was all because his mother chose to become involved with L. C. Underwood. He had to blame somebody. Someone had to be responsible for all of that loss, and Kay was the easiest and safest choice. She was the easiest because she was again the common denominator; she was the safest because Jason knew deep down that she would love him always and unconditionally.

Kay struggled with her relationship with Jason but was grateful she still had him with her. She felt safe when they were together at her mountain home. Kay told me she never had any unwanted guests and never had so much as an unknown car turn around in her driveway. But that all changed with one seemingly insignificant event.

As Kay drove along the scenic route to work one sunny morning, she rounded a curve to see a familiar vehicle parked on the shoulder of the highway. A man stood in front of the ugly old car with its two-toned panels of dark green and a lighter green. He was leaning against the car, looking down across the open farmland. He seemed to be trying to get his bearings. Or maybe he was waiting for someone.

Kay had always thought his was one of the ugliest cars she had ever seen and so easily recognizable, which was ironic considering his occupation. The man was Charlie Frick, and he was a private investigator from Salisbury. He was also a known friend, or at least an acquaintance, of L. C. Underwood. In fact, Kay told me she believed that Charlie had once worked for Salisbury P.D. and that he and L. C. had worked there together at some point.

Kay said she knew in an instant that Charlie Frick was trying to find her and report back to L. C. anything else that he could learn about her. She was told later by a mutual friend that L. C. was paying Charlie to give him detailed information on Kay's new life in Cullowhee, and in particular, to determine whether she was "having an affair" with someone or not. When Kay told me this, I called Charlie Frick's office in Salisbury and left messages, but Charlie never returned my calls. Kay never saw Charlie again, but that one sighting was enough to shatter her perceived bubble of security in Cullowhee.

"I'm moving," she told me one afternoon in 2003. "From Cullowhee."

"What? Not because of that P.I. Charlie Frick, I hope?"

"No, well, not entirely. There are other reasons."

"I thought you loved it there."

"I did, and in some ways I still do."

"I wouldn't let L. C. run me away from the home I loved, Kay," I told her.

"Well, it's not just that. Jason has graduated from Western, and he's got a job here working at an Irish Pub called O'Malley's, but he wants to move to northern Virginia where Matt, his father, lives. Matt says he can get him a job in his field."

"But what about his girlfriend? Are they still together?"

"Oh yes. Jason and Kalie are very much in love – even I can see that. Eventually she will move there too, I think."

"But what about your teaching at Western and at the community college out there?"

"Well, you've worked on the side as an Adjunct at Appalachian State, right?"

"Yes, I still do from time to time in the Criminal Justice Department."

"Well, you may know what I am referring to when I say that Adjuncts are treated differently than regular members of the faculty are treated."

"Differently in what ways?"

"Adjuncts don't get selected for committees or have other involvements, and I have been feeling recently that I am not a part of the university here in a way that I feel is meaningful to me other to than my students. I can't really attend the meetings and conferences and have a real voice in things here."

"Okay, but…"

"So, I decided to apply a few other places where I can eventually earn tenure and so forth. I just accepted a full-time offer to teach at Halifax Community College in Weldon."

"On the North Carolina coast," I replied.

"Yes. I'm putting my house on the market immediately."

"Wow. Well, first of all, congratulations on the new position. If you feel this will be a positive move for you, then I say good for you!"

"I think the change will be a positive one."

"I hope so, Kay. I really do."

"Speaking of change… They moved L. C. again. Did you know that?"

"No, I didn't. To where?" I asked.

"To Marion Correctional. I'd like to know why."

"Marion?" I repeated, instantly alert.

"Yes."

"When?"

"A few weeks ago."

"Marion in McDowell County, North Carolina?" I was incredulous. McDowell did not directly border Watauga County, but it was only one county over. It was only two counties away from Jackson County where Kay was currently residing.

"Yes, that's the place."

"Kay, is that also part of the reason you are moving from Cullowhee?" I asked, knowing the answer already.

"I can't deny that I will be glad to several hours away from L. C. Underwood," she said.

"Kay, you can't let L. C. or what they do with him determine the life decisions you make," I began.

She continued, "It's cold here in the mountains, and I'm not really used to it. It's beautiful in Weldon and Roanoke Rapids. It's near the Outer Banks on the Roanoke River, best fishing in the world!"

"Since when do you fish?" I asked her.

She ignored the question. "I'm looking forward to the milder temperatures, plus I will be that much closer to Jason and Kalie when they move." She sounded genuinely optimistic, and I did not want to say anything that might put a damper on that.

"Well, congratulations on your new position, then, and stay in touch."

"You know I will!" she replied.

CHAPTER NINE

**"This book of the law shall not depart out of thy
mouth; but thou shalt meditate therein day and night,
that thou mayest observe to do according to all that
is written therein: for then thou shalt make thy way
prosperous, and then thou shalt have good success."**
(Joshua 1:8)

About the time that Kay left Salisbury and moved to
Cullowhee, things changed for me as well. It was the spring
of 1998, and Captain Luther Harrison, the Chief Deputy,
highest ranking official under Sheriff Lyons, resigned from
the Watauga County Sheriff's Office to answer what he
believed was a spiritual calling by going to work for the
Billy Graham Ministries at Samaritan's Purse. He would be
sorely missed. Captain Harrison was a straight-up kind of
guy, hardworking, and always had a word of encouragement
for all of us working in the Department. I had no idea that,
upon his resignation, he had made a recommendation for his
replacement to Sheriff Lyons, not typically requested of nor
welcomed from a resigning senior member by an elected
official.

"I'm sorry to see Captain Harrison go," I told Sheriff
Lyons one Friday morning in his office.

"As am I. But he is doing what he believes the Lord has
called him to do, going to work for Samaritan's Purse and
all. He will get to do a lot of traveling, working on all those

mission trips and so forth. I believe he will serve the Graham ministries well; he will be a great asset for them."

"I'm sure he will," I replied.

"God is always working things out for the best," he commented. "Remember Romans 8:28."

"Yes, sir."

"He has plans for us even when we don't know anything about it. He does not take people from us, for instance, that He does not have someone else in mind to fill that void."

"I believe that."

"In this case, Detective Sergeant, both Luther and I believe that you are the one to fill the position of my Chief Deputy."

"*Sir?*"

"That's right. I asked Luther what his thoughts were on his replacement, and he strongly recommended you. You've worked hard to earn your way up the ranks to where you are now, and you've proven your diligence and dedication time and time again. Captain Harrison was particularly impressed with the grants you wrote; grants which have funded technology like the AFIS (automated fingerprint identification system) and the new radio system, technology we would not have in use here every day if it had not been for your work on those."

"I don't know what to say, Sheriff. I have not seriously considered the responsibility of commanding all the divisions, the whole Sheriff's Office. I'd worry that I wouldn't do a good job, that I'd make a mess of things somehow…"

"You know, Babe Ruth said, 'Never let the fear of striking out keep you from playing the game.' It applies to a lot of different situations."

I smiled. Sheriff Lyons was especially gifted at saying just the right thing to encourage, to motivate a person. He knew I relished a challenge.

He went on to say, "I know your heart is in investigations, and you are good at it. But you also have other skills we are lacking now at the command level, and I would like you to consider accepting the promotion."

I had not expected a promotional opportunity like that. The job responsibilities of Chief Deputy would be quite different from what my role had been for the past twelve years, and I felt unprepared for it. The Chief Deputy commanded the Criminal Investigations and Vice, but he/she also supervised all other divisions, which included Patrol, Administration, the Courts, Civil Process, 911 Emergency Communications, and the County Detention Center.

It was a lot to consider.

"Sheriff, I'd like to think about it – and pray about it – over the weekend. Can I give you an answer on Monday morning?" I asked.

"Yes, please do that."

On the following Monday morning, the sun shone brightly, but snowflakes wafted through the air. I wondered how that was possible when I saw only a few gray clouds in the otherwise-crystal-blue sky. I walked into the Sheriff's Office and brushed the large snowflakes off the shoulders of my winter coat as I stopped by my inbox, one of sixty or so wooden cubbyholes mounted on the wall in the officers' room. Inside was a memo on brown department letterhead, and I saw that the same brown memos were in everyone else's boxes as well. I carried it back to my desk and unfolded it.

Please join me in congratulating Det. Sgt. Paula May on her newest appointment as Chief Deputy. I trust you will support her as she begins her new responsibilities in this position effective this date.

Sheriffs in North Carolina have the ability to hire and fire at will, to appoint and remove whomever they wish to whatever position they wish, so long as there is no discriminatory basis. So much for waiting for my response on the promotion, I thought.

In early December of that same year, I was working at my desk when Patrol Sergeant Joe Moody knocked on my door. Joe was not only a shift sergeant on the road; he was also the firearms instructor, the range master, and the armorer for the Sheriff's Office.

"Sergeant Joe Moody," I said, smiling. "Good morning, Sir!"

"Good morning, Captain May," he said jovially. "It's a mite nippy out there this morning."

"Still? I've been here all morning working on our drug fund audit. I haven't been outside since early this morning."

"Yeah, but it's good and warm in here. I know you're busy, and I won't keep you. Just wanted to say good morning and bring you this from the post office," he said and handed me a white envelope. "I did the mail run and saw this, thought you might wanna see it right away."

I looked at the front of the envelope and recognized the handwriting immediately. I involuntarily bristled. My name and the address of the Sheriff's Office were handwritten on the front, and it was stamped Eastern Correctional Institution.

"It's from L. C. Underwood," I said.

"I hope he's not writing to threaten you," Sergeant Moody said. "...again." Even after all these years, Joe Moody, Del Williams, Hubert Townsend, Hobert Watson, Pat Baker, and other seasoned officers, who had been and were even yet protective of me to some degree. As the first female deputy sheriff and now the first female Chief Deputy in Watauga County, I did not resent their protective attitude; I appreciated it. If you want to grow smarter, and you're the smartest person in the room, you're in the wrong room. I had learned a lot from men like them, and I had plenty more to learn.

At the moment, I wanted to know the contents of the envelope Joe had just handed me.

"Let's find out what kind of games he's playing this week," I said, and opened it. It contained three pieces of lined legal pad paper, filled front and back with L. C.'s familiar handwriting.

Dear Detective May:

The letter I am writing concerns Lisa Collins. As you can confirm by speaking with my mother Barbara Childress, Lisa Collins has illegally obtained and used credit cards in my name. First of all, I never gave Ms. Collins permission or instructed her to obtain credit cards in my name, and never at any time was she authorized to use these cards by me. I knew absolutely nothing about the use of these cards until approximately three weeks ago, at which time my mother informed me. It is my understanding that one of these cards was from CCB and was used in the Boone – Blowing Rock area. The credit card # of the CCB card is as follows...

L. C. went on to describe several credit cards issued in his name which he alleged to have been used unlawfully by Lisa Collins without his permission to the tune of several thousand dollars.

"No threats here," I said to Sergeant Moody as he stood. "He's wanting help. He is reporting to me of all people that some female ripped him off, used his credit cards without his permission, you know the story. Some female by the name of Lisa Collins."

"If I'm not mistaken, she had charges here before. Spent some time in jail here, I believe."

"Really? Now that is something I shall look into shortly," I said. "Thank you."

"Want me to go search the jail files?" he offered.

"No thanks, I'll check them. If she was incarcerated when L. C. was in jail here, I will want to copy her whole file and see where she was housed in relation to him. It might take me a while. Thanks for offering, though, and for bringing the letter to me right away."

"No problem, ma'am," he said as he walked out the door.

"Stay warm, Sergeant!" I called after him. I read on.

Since my mother is my power of attorney, she applied for these cards in my name, which was fine. But since she did not even tell me about the cards, there is no way I could have authorized Lisa to use them.

After my mother cancelled the card from CCB, Ms. Collins applied for a credit card herself at Citibank in my name. Ms. Collins ran up thousands of dollars of credit card debt in my name, which my mother said a number of the charges were made in the Boone and Blowing Rock areas, and a few were made out of state. Again, I did not give her permission ever to do these things.

I was then informed by my mother on November 3, 1998 that Ms. Collins tried to use my BlueCross and BlueShield insurance card to charge $42 worth of services at some medical center in Blowing Rock, where I was told that she signed her name Mrs. L. C. Underwood. The letters I wrote to Lisa are mailed to P.O. Box 1581 in Boone. I don't actually know where she is living exactly. But I know she receives my letters because she tells me so in the letters I get from her. The last letter I got from Ms. Collins was on November 24, 1998.

L. C. stated that Lisa was on probation from New Hanover County, North Carolina, in the eastern part of the state. He went on to suggest that I go to the Boone Post Office and wait for her to come by and check her mail. Then I could arrest her for credit card fraud. He also asked me for something else.

I would prefer that you come here to the prison to speak with me about these matters personally. I will answer any questions you might have concerning Lisa Collins, and what I might know completely.

He ended the lengthy correspondence with feigned endearment, as he had always done when he wanted something. It turned my stomach.

Thank you for your assistance. I look forward to hearing from you. Very truly yours, L. C. Underwood.

Whatever Lisa Collins had done, it was not my responsibility, nor was it in my territorial jurisdiction. Had it been, it would be an appropriate matter for the detectives to handle, rather than me. A part of me wanted to go and see him, though. I suppose a part of me thought there was a slight chance he might say something more to me, something about Catherine Miller. Experience told me that would never happen.

It was a moot point to consider, in any event. Sheriff Lyons, A.D.A. Jerry Wilson, and SBI Agent Steve Wilson all thought it would be a bad idea and an unnecessary risk for me to take.

"You do remember the horrible things he said he wanted to do to you," Steve said.

Of course, I remembered. I knew well the depth of L. C. Underwood's hatred towards me, and now, in this letter, he had also insulted my intelligence with his attempts to charm me into complying with his oh-so-polite requests.

"Who knows what he's cooked up," Sheriff Lyons said. "He's had time to make friends with the guards, to line up deals and form alliances with other inmates, and I'd just rather you didn't put yourself at risk, to even be on the grounds at a medium security facility like that."

Thus, I did not go visit L. C. Underwood in prison, much to his disappointment. He could report his fraud to the Secret Service for investigation.

I was, however, curious about Miss Lisa Collins. As it turned out, both Lisa Collins and L. C. Underwood were in jail in Watauga County during the same period of time, between January and August of 1997. I took a large keyring from my desk drawer, stood up from my desk, and walked out, closing my office door behind me. Instead of walking down the hall to the jail office, I turned the opposite direction to the old narrow stairs that led to the musty basement.

Our older records – incident reports, arrest records, and jail records – were stored in a block wall room that was entirely underground. One lone lightbulb was all the illumination I had as I looked through the 1995 alphabetized files – the year Underwood was arrested. I found no jail records on a Lisa Collins in 1995. I moved to the cardboard file box marked 1996 and had flipped through the Cobles and the Cohns when one file caught my eye. It was a jail file for a white female, and the name neatly typed on the white label was Collins, Alisa B. It was the only folder in the 1996 files for a female with the last name Collins. I carried it back to my office. It was a relatively thick file, and I wanted to take my time perusing it.

Alisa B. Collins was welcomed to the Watauga County Detention Center in April of 1996 due to her criminal charges of Worthless Checks, Fraud, and Obtaining Property by False Pretenses. She must have been unable to make bond because she remained in jail awaiting trial until October of the same year. Alisa Collins or Lisa Collins, whatever her given name, was incarcerated in the jail in Watauga County during the same time that L. C. Underwood was awaiting trial for the kidnapping and murder of Viktor Gunnarsson.

A memory from the recesses of my mind floated to the forefront. I recalled talking with a blonde female named Lisa something-or-other years ago when she had been caught for writing a plethora of bad checks – no, *stolen* checks which she had written to herself and deposited into various accounts all controlled by her. Was I thinking about the same person? I believed so, but I could not be sure. There were so many. But I did recall that the girl had not been forthcoming with information at the time.

Having worked almost daily in my office only a short walk away from both of them, I had no idea that the two had met, much less that they had formed a romantic relationship, or at least as much of a romantic relationship as one can enjoy in a custodial setting where jail personnel were directed to lay eyes on every single inmate at least once per hour, every hour around the clock, at a minimum.

Given L. C.'s relentless desire to develop and maintain a close, intimate relationship with a woman whom he could manipulate, use, and control, I should not have been surprised to learn that he had developed a romantic relationship with this female inmate. Pickings for romance were slim in our rural county jail; so when the attractive 26-year-old Lisa arrived in custody with her blond hair, blue eyes, and keen wit, she must have attracted L. C.'s attention right away.

"I guess it was true jailhouse love," Steve commented when I told him what I suspected.

"Well, it explains how they met at least," I responded. "But I feel sorry for that poor girl, even if she did take him for a ride. She probably had no idea what kind of sociopath she was getting involved with."

"Maybe L. C. met his match, found someone that was more conniving than he was," Steve suggested. "Especially if she got hold of his credit cards."

"Maybe she just needed to buy a blender," I joked, remembering L. C.'s tacky habit of buying a blender – and only a blender – as a Christmas gift for each woman he had dated.

"Maybe she was buying him a cake she could slip a knife into," he said.

"If she ran up several thousand dollars like he said, that's a lot of cake and blenders."

"Don't you have to have a blender to bake a cake?" Steve asked. He had a mischievous glint in his eye. I assumed he was kidding.

"I'm gonna go out on a limb and say that you clearly have not baked a cake in quite some time," I responded.

"Never, in fact," he said.

"Uh-huh."

"So, you don't need a blender to bake a cake?" he asked.

"Rarely, if ever," I answered. "A mixer, yes. A blender, no."

"Aren't they the same thing?" Steve asked. Now he was messing with me.

"Not even close. I don't even own a blender myself. What if she knows something about Catherine Miller's murder, or the guns?" I wondered aloud. "What if she *has* one or all of them?"

"*All* of them?" Steve asked. "There were just two murders... that we know of."

"And a third attempt... the shooting into Jason's bedroom."

"Right," he remembered. "Not a chance, though," Steve said. "If that were the case, L. C. would not be trying to get her charged. He would be giving her anything she asked for if she had something like that hanging over him. She'd have him by the short hairs."

"I disagree. That is not how L. C. thinks. He is all about himself. Greedy. Controlling. Vengeful. He is more interested in revenge and punishment than he is about being charged with Catherine Miller's murder. I mean, he's already in prison for murder with a life sentence."

"She wouldn't say anything if she did know. Think about it. We've talked to just about every person L. C. has ever been close to, his ex-wives, his family members, his co-workers, and friends, and all he does is deny, deny, deny. He tells them all what SOB's we are and how we are framing him for these murders, so on and so on. I cannot imagine him telling some new girlfriend he met in jail up here that he killed either of them or telling her what he did with the guns."

"You're probably right," I relented. "But I just can't help but think he will tell someone what he did; someone, somewhere. He'll have to brag at some point. He is still a narcissist after all."

"We may not be around to know about it if he does," Steve said.

"Maybe *you* won't," I retorted. "But I've prayed about it. I asked God if he would give us a confession."

"From L. C. Underwood? That *will* take some divine intervention."

"That's no problem for God."

"Well, there's no denying the divine intervention we've had in this case already," Steve added.

I passed on the information about Alisa/Lisa Collins that I had found in the old files to Don Gale and Terry Agner. They were busy on other cases, other homicides, other violent crimes, but they did make an effort to locate Lisa to no avail. Besides, Steve was probably right; it was unlikely that she would be of any help to us. We would all have to wait on additional divine intervention.

CHAPTER TEN

"And then shall many be offended, and shall betray one another, and shall hate one another." (Matthew 24:10)

Only a few months had gone by since Don and Terry had tried unsuccessfully to locate Lisa Collins. It was early 1999 on a brutally cold day when dispatch informed me that I had a call they were about to transfer to me from the Rowan County Sheriff's Office. It was Terry.

Just as I was responsible for leading the investigation into Viktor Gunnarsson's murder in Watauga County, Detective Terry Agner was the lead investigator in the Catherine Miller murder case which had occurred in Rowan County. Although the cases overlapped and we investigated both cases together as a team, once L. C. Underwood was convicted and sentenced in the Gunnarsson case, there was really nothing left for me to do. In fact, there was nothing left for Don and Terry to do since D.A. Bill Kenerly had already made the decision not to proceed with charging L. C. with Catherine Miller's murder – that is, absent a discovery of new or additional evidence. But additional evidence was precisely what Don and Terry were after, nearly eight years after Catherine Miller was discovered shot to death inside her home.

"Hey, Terry! How are you?" I asked cheerily.

"Fine as frog hair," he said.

"That's pretty fine," I said, instantly recalling with disgust the large frog I had to dissect in my high school biology class, which I now realized had basically been an amateur autopsy. What a stream of consciousness. Its eviscerated, hairless, and tailless body had left an image in my mind I had not realized was permanently affixed. *Gross.*

"What's up?" I asked, trying to clear my mental image of the Anura amphibian autopsy.

"We found Lisa Collins," Terry told me.

"Not her deceased body, I hope!"

"No. She's alive and well in Women's Prison."

"Oh. Which one?" I asked.

"Women's Prison. Eastern part of the state. Fountain Correctional."

"How did you find her?"

"We didn't, actually. We had basically given up looking for her. But now, it seems, she got herself a prison sentence."

"How did you learn that?" I asked.

"She sent a letter to Don."

"No kidding."

"She did."

"Why?"

"We're…not sure."

"What did she say?"

"She said she had information she needed to get off her chest, or something to that effect."

"She didn't say what kind of information she has?" I asked. "I can't really imagine L. C. giving information to some other inmate, even a girlfriend. We tried so many times to get his friends to get something out of him…" I trailed off.

"I know. But she came to us. Maybe she got some information some other way or something, not through L. C."

"Maybe. But that seems far-fetched too."

"Most likely she's just wanting to jerk us around, blow some smoke and try to help herself get out of prison."

"Odds are. Or perhaps she's just after some good old-fashioned revenge."

"Yeah. Who knows?" Terry said. "We'll go see what she has to say anyway."

"She has certainly gotten *my* curiosity up."

"Ours too. Wanna come along?"

"No, not this time. Three's a crowd in the interview room. Besides, the Miller murder is your case; y'all deserve to get the goods first."

"Right," he said, chuckling.

"Keep me posted?" I asked.

"Like a sticky note," Terry replied as he disconnected the call.

I was glad that Terry and Don were following up with Lisa Collins, but I was not terribly optimistic about an alleged inmate, credit-card-thieving girlfriend of L. C.'s being much of a real help to the Miller murder investigation. If she did have anything to say, I feared that the Salisbury District Attorney, Bill Kenerly, would likely dismiss it with the argument that she would not make a credible witness in a trial; that is, if she was a regular customer of the correctional system in North Carolina. On the other hand, if she knew what L. C. had done with the murder weapon, the gun he used to kill Catherine, and we could somehow get our hands on it, now that was a different matter altogether.

That .38 caliber Colt Detective Special would be the one piece of tangible physical evidence that could gain us a jury trial. But there was no point in speculating such an unlikelihood.

On Friday, the fifth day of March 1999, Detective Terry Agner and Special Agent Don Gale drove nearly three hours eastward to Rocky Mount, North Carolina. They arrived at the Fountain Correctional Center for Women at approximately 1:00 in the afternoon. Don was dressed as he always did, in dark dress slacks, a long sleeve shirt, and tie. Terry was also smartly dressed, but less formally in khakis and a short sleeve polo with his name, title and badge embroidered on the chest. Both men locked their issued weapons in the trunk of the car before approaching the main prison entrance and signing in on the visitors' log.

Don and Terry were shown to a secure, private conference room in the inner prison, and a middle-aged prison matron escorted a blonde female of medium build over to them and instructed her to sit down across the table. She sat. The matron told Don and Terry she would be just outside the interview room if they needed anything.

"We'll be fine," Terry assured her. Don was watching the woman for any signs she might become problematic. He found none. She appeared to be calm but eager to talk with them. Or perhaps she had been in prison long enough to become eager to talk to anyone from outside the wall.

"I'll be just outside the door," the guard said. Terry nodded.

"Do you go by Lisa or Alisa?" Don asked, as he made a note of the date and time on a lined legal pad.

"No one calls me Alisa," she answered. "Lisa's fine."

Lisa Collins told them a few things they already knew, that she had been serving time at Fountain Correctional for only about two weeks thus far but had been an inmate in the North Carolina Department of Correction for four months, serving time for convictions of several counts of worthless checks.

"The Judge was only going to give me supervised probation, but I opted instead to do the time. There was no way I could pay restitution plus fees and fines both. I would owe way too much money," she told them bluntly.

Don nodded. Except for the rumble of voices and the occasional door banging outside the room, there was silence for a few moments.

"You were also in the Watauga County Detention Center a couple of years ago?" Don asked Lisa.

"Yes. Lamont and I were there at the same time," she said. "Late '96, into '97."

"Lamont Claxton Underwood?" Don asked, for clarification.

"Yes."

"About how long were you both there at the same time?" Don asked.

"A little over six months," Lisa said. "We got pretty close." She watched both of them for a reaction but found none.

"So did the two of you introduce yourselves and start talking then?" Terry asked Lisa.

"Something like that. But not at first. Once I did start talking to him, though, he would not shut up. I guess he was desperate for someone to talk to, someone to feel sorry for him, to admire him, ya know?"

How well they knew.

"He's a narcissistic son-of-a-gun," she said without emotion.

"That he is," Don said without further reaction.

"He hates you," Lisa said to Don.

"Old news," Don said, seemingly unconcerned. "What all did he discuss with you?"

"Everything under the sun. He loved to talk about himself – what all he had done in his cop career and all that. And then he told me."

"He told you what, exactly?" Don asked.

"That he killed them."

"That he killed who?" Terry asked.

"Lamont told me he killed two people," Lisa said. "Well, he didn't actually say that he *only* killed two people now that I think about it. But Lamont – well, I know y'all call him *L. C.* but I call him Lamont – yes, he told me about killing the Swedish man and Kay's mama, Mrs. Miller, how he did it and all that. He talked *nonstop*. Sometimes I just had to tell him to shut up. Eventually I got tired of hearing about it. At first, though, it intrigued me."

"Was anyone else nearby when he told you these things? Could anyone else ever hear what he was saying, what he was telling you?"

"No. We were on a completely different cell block, or hall, from everybody else. We were closer to the front of the jail, closer to the office where they could watch us better, I guess. I was in a female dorm cell, but I was the only female, and he was the only one in a single cell in the jail for a long time."

"Okay. And you are now willing to tell us what all he said to you?" Terry asked.

"I am."

"Why, Lisa?" Don asked bluntly, as he often spoke.

"Because I'm tired of carrying around all that baggage with me," she responded. "It's not right, him getting away with killing that little old lady, Kay's mama."

Don and Terry were both silent for a few moments, studying her.

"Look, I know I'm no saint, not by a long shot. But I am not a murderer, and I don't believe in taking someone's life like that. I do have my standards," she said defensively.

"We aren't here to judge you, Lisa," Don said.

"Yes, you are. You're judging me now. Trying to figure out if I'm telling the truth or not. But I am. Every word, whether you believe it or not."

"And are you only doing this now out of the goodness of your heart?" Don asked.

She didn't answer.

"Why are you telling us now?" Terry asked.

"Because it's been bothering me. I, I should have told you back then."

"Why didn't you?"

"I thought that I loved him. There was a time I would have done or said anything to protect him."

"Like what would you do?" Don asked.

"Like anything he asked me to do," she said, frankly.

"What changed?" Don asked.

"I found out he isn't capable of loving anyone. He just wanted to use me."

"Now that's the Lamont we all know and love," Terry said.

"Like I said, I would have done anything for him at one time, and I thought he would do anything for me. But then he tried to get me in trouble for using some credit cards that he gave me and *told me* to use. Him and Bobbie. You know who Bobbie is, right? The woman he calls his mother."

"In Ohio."

"Yes. She's not his mother, though. She definitely is *not* his mother," Lisa said with disgust.

"No, she isn't his mother," Don agreed.

"I don't want to talk about her though. I hate her."

"Why's that?" Don asked.

"I said I don't want to talk about her."

"Alright then. What did L. C. – sorry – *Lamont* tell you that you are willing to share with us?" Don asked Lisa.

"First he told me about killing that Swedish man…"

"And did he call him by name?"

"Yes, Viktor Gunnarsson. And then he told me about killing Kay's mama."

"Kay Weden's mother?"

"Yes, he called her Catherine. Kay's mother, Catherine Miller."

"Okay. Please tell us what you can remember then."

"Oh, I remember it very well," she said. "At first, like I said, he just talked. He rambled on about this and that, flirting with me, and just rambling on and on. It took him about a month, maybe two, to instill his trust in me, I guess. But then, as he started talking with me about his case, you know, the evidence against him and all that, Lamont started telling me bits and pieces about the murders."

"You mean as he became more comfortable talking with you?"

"Yeah. And we had kind of started having a relationship by then..."

"A romantic relationship?"

"Yeah. Well, as romantic as you can be in jail," she said and laughed. "Although you wouldn't believe what all can be accomplished in a jail if a person sets their mind to it."

"Yes, we would," Don and Terry responded again simultaneously.

"Okay. I'm going to tell you everything that I can remember..." she said.

CHAPTER ELEVEN

**"Nay, ye do wrong, and defraud, and that
your brethren." (I Corinthians 6:8)**

In early 1997, Lisa Collins was arrested for Obtaining Property by False Pretenses. She could not post the bond set by the Magistrate, so she was incarcerated in the Watauga County Detention Center while she awaited trial. After she was booked and the few personal items she had with her were locked up, Lisa was issued one white towel, one white washcloth, one scratchy wool blanket, one bright orange one-piece unisex jumpsuit, and one pair of rubber flip-flops. Prohibited items were any types of belts, shoelaces, or any other item she could theoretically use to assault another person, start a fire, build a bomb, pick a lock, slash her wrists, electrocute, or hang herself.

Lisa was led down the hallway to the first section on the right of the jail. Down that hall, the barred cells on the left were reserved for females only. The cells on the right, closest to the jailer's office, were single cells, reserved for problematic inmates who did not play well with others, or who were charged with particularly violent crimes. The jail smelled of recently administered chlorine bleach and other chemical cleaners, not altogether unpleasant when one considered the odors some such institutions reeked of, such as the stench of sweat, vomit, urine, and other unsavory human filth. Lisa could live with the antiseptic odor, and she hoped her cell had been wiped or sprayed down since its last occupant departed.

Lisa stepped inside her steel-barred cell and took a mental inventory of its furnishings. It did not take long. The cell contained one steel, wall-mounted bunk with a plain mattress pad atop it, a wall-mounted writing desk with matching cement bench, a stainless-steel commode, a small wall-mounted stainless steel sink, and a block shower stall devoid of shower door, rod, or curtain. A small, round drain cover adorned the middle of the hard, gray floor. The bang of the steel door echoed as it was closed and locked behind her. She was alone inside her windowless cell.

She sat down on her bunk and sighed, only to look up and see a pair of unusually dark brown eyes peering at her from diagonally across the hall. His single cell was not directly across from hers, but when they both leaned forward on the bars, they could see each other plainly. Lisa was in no mood for socializing. The single cell was occupied at the time by a Caucasian man with very dark brown eyes rimmed with black lashes but no visible laugh lines. The man must be in jail for something serious because he was assigned to a single cell, away from the rest of the male population who were housed in dorm cells further down the long hallway. Lisa could hear the others talking, laughing, arguing, and occasionally brawling, but they were not near enough for her to make heads or tails of the subject matters, nor did she care to know.

Lisa learned that the man in the single cell was awaiting trial for the murder of Viktor Gunnarsson, which fact she absorbed initially from the jailers and the other inmates when she was led out of her cell for her daily exercise and fresh air. She had not yet met him directly, and she was not looking for companionship, as she had her own state of affairs to contemplate. She did note, however, that the man in the single cell was not hard on her eyes.

Lisa and L. C. Underwood did not exchange pleasantries immediately, but she sensed that he spent a lot of his time watching her, not that there was anything else to see besides the four walls and whatever occasional correspondence he received. L. C. had already read every magazine and lame book the jail library had to offer. The "library" was little more than a storage closet that housed a collection of books so worn and out of date they were of little interest to anyone. Most inmates used the books for purposes other than reading, such as tearing out the pages and rolling cigarettes or any other substance they could get smuggled in to smoke.

Fortuitously, someone feeling something akin to generosity around the recent holidays happened to donate an issue of Readers' Digest that was only a couple of months old, and L. C. had it in his cell, reading it.

"Hey! Have you ever heard of the Ebola Virus?" the man called across the hallway to her.

She looked up to make sure he was talking to her and not a jailer.

"Not much," she said, but she thought, *Okay, weirdo, let's see what this is about...*

"It's deadly as h*ll," he said.

"Oh really?" Lisa asked him, not particularly interested in the subject matter.

"Yeah."

"It's a type of food poisoning, right?" she offered.

"Yes, it is. It says here that it's one of the worst kinds of food poisoning. First you get a high fever, vomiting, and diarrhea. Then when it gets all throughout your system, you just start bleeding from everywhere, inside, and out. You bleed from your organs, and it comes out your ears, mouth, and eyes."

"Sounds like a good time," Lisa responded.

"Yeah," he laughed, "a real good time."

"What kind of food?" she asked.

"Huh?"

"How does it get into food?"

"It says that Ebola virus is transmitted from animals such as monkeys, gorillas and bats through their blood, secretions, and meat."

"Who eats monkey or bat meat?" Lisa asked.

"It may be what they're feeding us here," he joked.

Lisa laughed. "Hey, I got no complaints about the food here," she said. "Trust me... it could be so much worse. I've had way worse. This is the Ritz compared to some places I've been, like New Hanover and J. Ruben Long. They were horrible."

"What were you in those places for?" he asked tentatively.

"Bad checks."

"Oh. I'm Lamont. I know your name already. You're Lisa." She nodded.

"Who told you my name?" she asked.

"I have my sources," he said, trying to sound mysterious. "I've never been on this side of the bars before," he told her. "I have nothing to compare it to."

"You're in jail for murder and you've never been in jail before? For anything?"

"No. I've never even had a traffic ticket. ...I've given out plenty of them though."

"Traffic tickets?"

"Yeah."

"What... You were some kind of cop of something?"

"H*ll, I got twenty years of being a cop under my belt."

"Are you serious?" she asked.

"Yes," he said.

"What were you, a state trooper?"

"H*ll no! Don't insult me like that. Troopers are just glorified traffic cops."

"Well, were you a city cop or a sheriff's deputy or what?"

"Yes to both. I've been a deputy *and* a city cop. H*ll, I was a detective for years."

"Then you shouldn't have gotten caught," she boldly pointed out.

"I didn't do anything to get caught for," he retorted. "For the past eight years, I was with Salisbury PD, well, up until right before I got arrested on these trumped-up charges. ... They're trying their best to frame me," he added.

"Right," she said, "because everyone locked up in here is innocent," she said sarcastically.

"Well, *I* am," he said.

"Then you didn't kill the man they're saying that you killed?"

"H*ll, I never even heard of the man. He's not even an American. I never met him, never saw him before in my life…"

"Who killed him then?" she challenged him.

"H*ll if I know! They think he killed the Prime Minister of Sweden. That's where he's from. They even arrested him for it over there. He got the charges dropped somehow, and then he took off. I have no idea how he ended up in Salisbury, North Carolina."

"Well, they must have *something* linking him to you," Lisa argued pointedly.

"They're trying to say that because he was dating my ex-girlfriend that I kidnapped and murdered him out of jealousy."

"Sounds about right," Lisa teased.

"I was on a date myself the night he disappeared."

"So, you have an alibi."

"Sort of. She wasn't with me all night. She had to work the next morning."

"Oh. Is she your girlfriend?" Lisa asked.

"No. Just someone I dated when I didn't have anything better to do."

"Or anyone?"

"Pardon?"

"Or when you didn't have any*one* better to do?"

"Something like that," he said and laughed. "Nah, she was a nice lady. Just more of a friend than a girlfriend," he added.

"They gotta have some kind of evidence against you," Lisa argued. "Cops don't just arrest another cop for murder out of the blue."

"You really wanna hear about my case?" he asked her, looking at her intently.

"Sure. It's not like I have anywhere else I gotta be."

"Maybe you can help me figure out how to prove I didn't do this."

"Maybe," she responded.

Over the next several days, L. C. took every available opportunity to try and convince Lisa that he was not guilty of murder. He was more successful in his efforts to charm her with his smooth-talking manner and to impress her with his wildly embellished heroic accomplishments as a law enforcement officer than he was in convincing her that he was innocent of any foul play concerning Viktor Gunnarsson's definitive demise. Yet she continued to give him audience, and she read nearly every document he had in his possession concerning the case that continued to mount against him.

There was the evidence, and then there was Lamont himself, the man standing before her day and night, entrusting her with his confidential communications with his attorneys, showering her with compliments and pouring out his heart only to her. Accordingly, Lisa could not deny the chemistry between them, the sheer physical attraction they shared. The quantities of dopamine, norepinephrine, and oxytocin released from each of their brains to the rest of their bodies made them giddy, providing them each with energy and excitement in an environment that was anything but. The chemicals were the likely culprits that prompted L. C. to share more with Lisa than he had ever shared with anyone before.

Thus L. C. and Lisa grew close, their relationship solidified by the commonalities of the rather bleak situations they each were facing. It was the two of them against the rest of the world, a classic formula for bonding. Lamont told Lisa about his childhood, how he was cruelly abandoned by both of his parents, and physically and mentally abused by his paternal uncle. In addition to being physically attracted to him, Lisa felt sorry for him, at least for the neglected and abused little boy that he had been. She understood his deep-seated fear of rejection and could see how it had affected his less than appropriate behavior in his adult relationships. But in a restricted environment where he could not hurt her and no one else was around to warn her against it or to interfere, she could be free to love him as he was and accept whatever kind of love he could give her in return. At the very least, they could keep each other occupied for the here and now.

Lisa and L. C. spent nearly seven months communicating both verbally and nonverbally with each other while being separated by two sets of steel bars, forming a bizarre romantic relationship that held little promise of a future. They filled their days by poring over copies of the search warrants executed on L. C.'s property, copies of interviews, and eventually the entire prosecution summary I had spent weeks preparing for the prosecution. Although she wanted to believe that he was not guilty of kidnapping a total stranger and shooting him to death in cold blood, Lisa sensed that he was lying to her, at least about the murder if not everything else he told her about himself. Finally, she confronted him.

"Lamont, there is a lot of information here, evidence that points to your guilt," Lisa began.

"It's all B.S.," he summarily announced to Lisa.

"No, it isn't all B.S., Lamont."

"Most of it is. It's what those four – well mostly Don Gale and Paula May – have conjured up to frame me," he said dismissively.

"Listen to me, Lamont," Lisa countered. "I need you to be real with me."

"Lisa, I've been more real with you than anybody I've ever met in my entire life!" he said in raised voice.

"Shhhhh! Just calm down! I know you have, and I'm trying to help you. But you have got to be honest with me, Lamont."

"I *am* being honest with you, Lisa. I, I, I didn't want to tell you like this, but I'm gonna tell you now anyway. I love you, Lisa. I think I fell in love with you the first day I saw you."

"I know, Lamont."

"You know what? That I love you?" he asked.

"Yes. I can tell that you love me."

"Well, do you love me?" he asked.

She met his dark eyes. "Yes, I do. I love you. And that's the reason I need you to be one hundred percent honest with me. You know I would never do anything to hurt you. You know that, don't you, Lamont? You can trust me."

"I know I can trust you," he told her.

"Then tell me the truth, Lamont, about everything. We can't move forward until you do."

"I've told you..."

But Lisa cut him off. She was not going to be lied to, not by him, not by anyone. She was no dummy.

"Look, Lamont... I get that you hate Don Gale and that he hates you. I get that you hate Paula May too, for telling the judge all that stuff about your old girlfriends at your bond hearing and getting him to keep you here with no bond. But do you honestly think Detective May pulled hair out of Viktor Gunnarsson's head when they found his body in the snow and then later attached it somehow into the fiber of your car's trunk mat? They didn't even identify the body until days later!"

"I know, but there was the autopsy..."

"Don't interrupt me, Lamont. We need to get this out in the open so we can talk about it and move on. I can't move on until we do," she said.

"Okay, Honey."

"And Detective May did not even go to the autopsy. That was Agent Wilson, remember?"

L. C. nodded.

"And he did not even know who the body was at the autopsy. So, if you're trying to say that one of those two pulled his head hairs at the scene or at the autopsy to frame you with later – and neither one of them had ever even met you before, right?"

"As far as I know, but…"

"I'm right. They didn't even know your name, so why would they take hair to frame somebody with later for murder? It makes no sense, Lamont. And it won't make sense to no jury either."

L. C. looked around the room, attempting to formulate an intelligent response.

Lisa was not finished. "And Shirley Twitty, your date on that Friday, the third of December… She took the investigators back to the house where you got the tag number, and it was Kay's house. Your *alibi* for the night Viktor Gunnarsson went missing gave a statement to the investigators that she was basically helping you stalk Kay Weden and that you had her write down Viktor Gunnarsson's tag number. Then you went back to your house and called your deputy friend Rick and asked him to run it for you, and he did!"

"I know, but the address he gave me…"

"Stop lying to me, Lamont. You went to his apartment and arrested him or whatever to get him in your car, didn't you?"

He did not respond.

"Lamont, look at me! I know you did. Look, I understand. I know how you think, and how hurt you must have been."

"I didn't love her like I love you," he said, as if that explained everything.

"I'm not talking about me, about us," she said. "I want to know I can trust you to tell me the truth, and that you can trust me. It's the only way we're gonna work, that our relationship can work, under these circumstances."

He pressed his lips tightly together, breathed in heavily, and exhaled with a sigh. Against everything he had learned as a cop about keeping his mouth shut, he capitulated to Lisa.

"What do you want to know?" he asked her and sat down heavily on his bunk.

"I want to know everything," she said. "Start from the beginning, and remember, you can trust me. I love you, Lamont."

"I love you too, honey. I really do. You will never know just how much I do love you."

"Okay, Lamont. Now tell me the truth. All of it."

No other inmates were on their hallway, so for the next several hours and well into the night, L. C. quietly described to Lisa how he had forced Viktor Gunnarsson from his apartment and into L. C.'s car, driven him to Deep Gap, and shot him in the dark woods near the Blue Ridge Parkway. She committed the details to memory as he spoke, not to betray him with, but to understand better the man who now claimed to love her.

"I can understand all that, Lamont," she told him. "Gunnarsson was probably a murderer himself, an assassin even."

"Oh yeah," L. C. agreed, not even pretending to feel remorse for killing Viktor.

"So, you killed Kay's mother too."

L. C. did not answer her right away, but finally, as he continued to stare downward at the old tile floor, he answered her. "I didn't mean to," he said.

"You mean it was an accident? You accidentally shot Kay's mother... twice?"

"Not exactly," he said.

Most days and nights, "Lamont" was the only person with whom Lisa spoke for any significant amount of time. This fact alone made L. C. grow more confident, more trusting of Lisa, who, after all, had not talked to any investigators, even about her own charges. As time went on, he told her more and more details about the things that he had done. L. C. had finally begun to relax, to adapt to his environment in the jail, and to the system – the way things were done inside the block walls of the Watauga County Detention Center.

The Chief Jailer at the time, Mike Long, was "chill," rather laid-back and kind to the inmates overall, at least as kind as they would allow him to be. He could be funny, too, and stern and loud if he needed to be. Lisa found Mike to be a fair man, and the others nicer than most jailers and guards she had ever met. She was particularly fond of a jailer by the name of Danny who prayed with her one night when she was feeling especially low.

Lisa contended with her bouts of depression in one unusual way. She began to draw very large, intricately detailed angels on the walls of her jail cell. Crayons were all the inmates were allowed to have (since one sharpened pencil made for an effective shank), but Lisa used them to their fullest potential. One angel in particular that she drew above her bed was visible to L. C. from his cell. She later commented, *"I covered the walls with them. I can't explain the reasoning behind it then or what my thoughts were. I just felt compelled to do it and they would bring me comfort.... and they did. Several times Mike (Long) had me color over them, but I always just began again and eventually, he gave up...there was no turning back from loving Lamont, and I prayed God would protect me in loving this man. I prayed for the wrong reasons, asked for the wrong things...and God was silent."*

The jailers were pretty lenient, and sometimes that resulted in them being less cautious than they should have been, in Lisa's eyes. Lisa and the other inmates knew that Sheriff Red Lyons, Paula May, and the others were always preaching safety and warning the jailers against being so chummy with the inmates. Lisa knew that the first time any of the inmates got angry and turned on them, well, it would not be good. Lisa thought they took too many chances, that they were not careful enough around the inmates. She observed as some of the jailers left themselves vulnerable to them at times, not that she had any intention of hurting any of them. She pretty much had it made as far as jail accommodations went, she admitted to herself. She had free room and board, the food wasn't bad, and the jailers allowed her to spend more time outdoors in the "yard" than she was supposed to spend. They got away with it because she offered to wash windows, pull weeds, and perform other tasks that kept her outside.

After some persuasion, Lisa even talked one or two of the jailers into allowing Lamont outside with her, who claimed that his cell was not of adequate size for him to walk or perform his physical therapy exercises to keep his back from aching. It was during those times that they even had opportunity for limited physical contact, such as a hug or a kiss. It was enough to keep progressing their relationship forward.

Lisa overheard a couple of the female jailers talking. In a safety meeting, Paula May had apparently shown them some of the gruesome crime scene photos of murders that the inmates in the jailers' care had allegedly committed. She was trying to make the point that they did not know who they were dealing with in the jail, they did not know the details of the cases or the horrific acts that had been committed against other human beings, and that they needed to take their roles seriously. Lisa did not see a great deal of improvement, however. As she saw it, as long as they were decent to her, she would be decent to them. The problem was that other inmates did not see it as a quid pro quo relationship. Some were only looking for a chance to get some attention, make a name for themselves, escape, or exercise their violent tendencies.

An incident had occurred recently where one of the jailers had been attacked by a prisoner serving jail time who very nearly escaped. A special meeting was called, and Sheriff Lyons was furious.

"This is not a schoolyard playground!" he scolded loudly. "And these people are not your playmates! Right this minute, there are inmates in this facility that would just as soon shove a shank in your neck and watch you bleed out than to get an extra dessert at mealtime!" Sheriff Lyons's face was as red as a pickled beet. He was a stickler for safety and for operating by the book. Sheriff Lyons was mad, but he was even more afraid when he realized how close one of them had come to being killed, and his adrenaline was pumping.

A couple of other female jailers were also perhaps overly sympathetic towards the inmates, and as Lisa and other inmates had often discussed privately, there were a few jailers who took an awful lot of unnecessary chances, opportunities that could easily have gotten themselves and the inmates all killed. Lisa observed several poorly managed maneuvers made by the jailers assisting Lamont, but Lisa decided that if they did not care then she certainly did not. She was unafraid of him at that point, even if he had gotten released on bond before his trial.

In any event, by the summer of 1997, Lisa had gotten to know Lamont Underwood much better, probably as well as any woman ever really got to know the man he really was.

"We were only a matter of a few feet from one another," Lisa would explain to me much later. "We could see and hear each other clearly. We could certainly pass anything between us, and we did... Books, notes, letters, t-shirts and boxer shorts, candy, and drinks. Things that one of the female jailers would buy from the local Walmart with cash our families sent us and bring down on this trolley. To any of the inmates, really. Not a lot of people stayed long in the jail, though. They were in and out in a day or two...

"The only person I can think of that stayed for a long time was a man named Kenneth Coffey. He was rude, crude and mean. He and another man named Bobby Bragg murdered an elderly man in town by bludgeoning him with a trailer hitch."

"Marvin Coy Hartley," I recalled.

"What?" Lisa asked.

"The elderly man they murdered. His name was Marvin Coy Hartley. He lived in a mobile home behind Walmart in Boone."

"Yeah, yeah, that's his name. Kenneth Coffey thought he was really something for doing that. He had already been convicted but was brought back to the jail for some kind of hearing or something. Anyway, I thought what they did to that old man was very cowardly, very unnecessary, and just evil. I don't even know why they did it because that poor old man didn't have nothing worth taking. Lamont hated Kenneth Coffey and threatened to kill him all the time. It was all insanity, all the violence and talk of killing always, but it was my reality at the time," Lisa recalled. "Things look vastly different from inside a cell. You are trapped and you adapt, or you kill yourself. It was systematic conditioning by circumstances. It's just the way it was then. "...Lamont was calm and mostly non-problematic for them, for the jailers. I heard Mike Long tell Lamont one day that I could stay in the cell across from him as long as there weren't any problems. I'm sure if I had objected in any way or raised a problem, they would have moved me. I realize things are not like that anymore. There are a lot more safety features in place, as there should be. But things were different for all of us back then...."

"What *was* L. C. really like?" I asked Lisa.

"Honestly, he was...evil on the inside. And I have been in the presence of many evil people, not only Lamont, but the people that cannot be reached in any way. I pray for them now but most if not all that I have encountered, including many women, they should never, ever, *ever* be allowed back into society. They don't value life at all, not human life, not even the lives of animals. You probably know this already, but there is a darkness there in the eyes of evil, where no light can ever shine. Lamont had these real dark brown, nearly black eyes. They had no light in them at all. All the sinister, evil people I've known have that same trait in common, there being no light in their eyes. It's a sad and frightening common denominator."

CHAPTER TWELVE

**"These six things doth the LORD hate: yea,
seven are an abomination unto him:
A proud look, a lying tongue, and hands
that shed innocent blood, an heart that
deviseth wicked imaginations, feet that be swift
in running to mischief, a false witness
that speaketh lies, and he that soweth discord
among brethren." (Psalm 6:16-19)**

Don and Terry continued to interview Lisa on the days following their initial visit to the women's penitentiary in 1999.

Lisa was still willing to answer their questions.

"You were sharing with us how L. C. – I'm sorry, how *Lamont* – talked freely with you about the murders," Don reminded her.

"Yes. We were in jail together, more or less across from one another, for about six months before his trial started in Boone. I remember because we were talking about the evidence y'all had against him and how he and his lawyers were gonna defend it. I don't remember the one lawyer's name, but I do remember his other lawyer, Bruce Kaplan. Anyway, L. C. went on and on and on about his case once he got started."

"I can imagine," Don and Terry said, in stereo.

Lisa smiled for the first time.

"He kept talking about it even after he was convicted."

"You mean before he went to prison?" Terry asked.

"Yes, but mostly when I visited him at Eastern."

"Eastern Correctional in Maury, North Carolina?" Don asked.

"Yes."

"How many times did you visit him there?"

"Four or five, I guess."

"Lisa, to be perfectly clear, are you saying that L. C. – Lamont – specifically told you that he killed Viktor Gunnarsson and Catherine Miller both or just what the evidence was against him?" Don asked.

"I told you already. Lamont confessed to killing both of them! And I also know he hasn't been charged with killing Catherine Miller. That's why I had to tell you."

"Alright. Go on, please."

"Like I said, he told me all this over a period of time. But Lamont said that the day he killed Catherine Miller, he drove to her house in that burgundy-colored car he has, that Monte Carlo. It's a Monte Carlo. He said he drove to her house in that car, but she wasn't there, so he left and came back about twenty minutes later." She paused while Don continued writing on his legal pad.

"Go on," he said.

"He said he knocked on Mrs. Miller's door, and she answered it. Of course, she knew him, and she let him in. Oh, and Lamont said he heard a beep when she opened the door, like she turned off the alarm or something."

"When she opened the door or when they went inside the house and she closed the door?"

"I'm not sure. He just said he heard a beep like she had turned off the alarm."

"Okay. Did he say that he specifically went there to kill her?"

"Uh, well, no. He said he went there to get some money that she owed him or that Kay owed him or something. I think he said Kay owed the money, but Catherine was gonna pay it back or something like that. Anyhow, they got into an argument about the money, and Lamont said he backed her up against something in the kitchen. She grabbed his arm and started yelling, and Lamont said he pushed her away and shot her. He said he shot her in the head, and then she slumped down against something in the kitchen, like the refrigerator maybe or the counter or something…" Lisa paused to take a breath.

"He pushed her away and then shot her in the head?" Don asked.

"Well, he said she grabbed his arm and that's when he pushed her backward and I guess shot her at the same time. But then, when she slumped down against the refrigerator or whatever it was, then (sic) he shot her again to make sure she was dead!"

"In the head? He shot her a second time in the head?" Don asked.

"Yes, to make sure she was dead, he said."

"What else did he say? What other details do you remember that he told you?"

"Oh, he said that right before he shot her, she asked, Catherine asked him why he was doing that, and then he shot her. And before that, before she said that, she threatened to call the police on him, when they were arguing about the money."

All three of them were silent for a few moments.

Then Don said, "What other details can you recall about that specific incident? Anything at all?"

"Yeah. He also said she was cooking something on the stove when he got there."

"Did he say what she was cooking?"

"I don't remember. But I asked him if he parked in her driveway, and he told me that he didn't park in her driveway because he thought if Catherine saw that it was him, she might not answer the door."

"Where did he park then?" Terry asked.

"He said he parked on the road, either beside her house or, wait… no, actually he said somewhere on a road behind her house. Is there a road behind and in front of her house both?"

"Yes, there is."

"That's not paved? He said it wasn't a paved road."

"That's correct."

"He said the road he parked on wasn't paved, and he parked away from her house and walked. But I don't know how far away. He didn't say how far. But it must not have been too far. Probably a block or two, I'd say."

"Did he mention anything else that happened in the house? Was there a struggle anywhere besides the kitchen?" Don asked.

"I don't think there was much of a struggle anywhere except that he said she grabbed his arm. I'm not sure why she grabbed his arm, but that made him mad apparently. But he wanted to make it look like a robbery, so he said he threw some magazines around the house. But he didn't steal nothing. Well, he said he didn't take any jewelry from her body because he didn't want to touch her. But he did take her wallet, some credit cards, and maybe her checkbook, but he threw them all out of his car window."

"Did he say *where* he threw those things out?"

"No, he said it was just some drug neighborhood in Salisbury. I guess he knew where all the crack neighborhoods and places were, being a cop there and all."

"Lisa, do you know, or did Lamont say what gun he used to shoot Catherine Miller?"

"Yeah, he said it was his .38. A revolver."

"Did he say where he got the gun?"

"Where it came from? No, he didn't say."

"Do you remember anything else he may have said about the Miller murder at all?"

"I think that's it. I don't remember anything else other than what I just told you."

"Okay then. Why don't we take a little break, stretch our legs, use the restroom, get some water, whatever."

"Y'all need to make a phone call?" Lisa asked.

"That too," Don said.

I answered the direct line in my office. It was Terry.

"Hey! How's it going? What are you into today?"

"Just living the dream," I told him. "Having any luck down there?"

"We are." Terry talked rapidly and caught me up to speed while they were on a brief break.

"Wow. Well good for Lisa! Finally... someone with some information. Wait, though... Do you think he really told her all that or do you think she's just read about it in the newspapers?" I asked.

"Don and I were just talking briefly about the possibility that she is just looking for a way out of trouble. And she may be looking for some assistance. She hasn't asked us for anything yet. But whatever her motivations are, she comes across as truthful. She isn't hesitant in her answers, and she does know some facts that were never released. She may not be telling us everything, but she is telling us a lot."

"Well, great then. That sounds very promising. Will she also tell you about Viktor? I still have some unanswered questions."

"She's just about to, I believe. I will call you after," Terry assured me.

"Okay, go on then, and I'll just wait to hear back. Thanks for keeping me posted."

"Like a sticky note, I told you."

Lisa was brought back to the small conference room. She recounted to Don and Terry the details of Viktor Gunnarsson's murder just as she claimed that L. C. – Lamont – had conveyed them to her...

CHAPTER THIRTEEN

"For jealousy is the rage of a man: therefore he will not spare in the day of vengeance." (Proverbs 6:34)

L. C.

He hated most holidays, but he especially despised the ones which begged large family gatherings. Ironically, L. C. Underwood was thankful that Thanksgiving had come and gone in 1993. He had been following Kay at a distance for the past week. In truth, he had been stalking her for some time, even before she showed up at the seafood restaurant with that loser she met on the internet. She was so stupid, thinking she was going to find a real man on a computer, a man that would love her like he could, a man that would not tire of meeting her frivolous demands.

L. C. was fairly certain he would not be bothered with him again, though. He chuckled to himself as he remembered the look of shock on the face of Kay's date when he dumped that entire glass of iced tea in Kay's lap. Then, when he got in his face, the man just leaned back like he wanted to bolt, like a scared rabbit. No, he would not be bothering either of them again. L. C. had probably done him a favor if the truth were known.

L. C. was not even sure why he could not get Kay out of his head. He loved and hated her with the same intensity. Kay was always whining about something, rattling off about some boring thing going on at the high school where she worked. Sometimes he just wanted her to shut the h*ll up.

He did not even know why he even still gave two bits about what she did. But she had told him many times that she loved him; she had said those words to him that he so needed to hear. He needed someone in his life to care about him. He needed to mean something to someone, especially a woman. He just did not understand how she could love him as she had claimed and still treat him the way she did. She would pay for that somehow, he thought. No woman was going to get away with hurting him again. Not ever.

For a while, Kay had been easy to control, easy to manipulate. She was so trusting, so naïve. She seemingly had no clue that it was he, the very man she claimed to love, the very man with whom she would climb into bed, who was doing the things to her that made her afraid, that made her seek him out for comfort and protection. L. C. just shook his head in disbelief when he recalled the things he had done to shake her up a little bit, to give her a dose of the real world so she would realize she needed him and his protection. He could admit to himself that he enjoyed seeing her stress and worry to some degree because she deserved it, in a way. She deserved to have a taste of what he had gone through in life. He was doing her a favor, in fact, by opening her eyes to the real world and what could happen.

He allowed himself to recall the terror in her voice when she called to tell him about the "anonymous" threatening phone calls she and Jason were receiving. He recalled the horror on her face when she showed him the "anonymous" threatening letters. He recalled the helplessness in her eyes the day she found the spray-painted messages in her garage, all over her new car, and on the exterior of her garage door for all the world to see what she was. Each time she had consistently run to him for comfort, just as he had known she would.

Still, her arrogance and naivete remained. One of the things that infuriated him the most at present was her apparent lack of concern for him with regard to his dying mother. He dwelled on that a great deal. True, his mother was not really dying. For that matter, she was not even his mother, not even close. She was – well, it was kind of hard to say what Bobbie was to him now exactly. She had been *a lot* of things to him since he met her, had served a variety of purposes to him along the way. None of that was any of Kay's business, though.

As far as Kay knew, Bobbie was a mother figure in L. C.'s mind, and that should have been enough. If Bobbie w*as* dying, then Kay should have been a lot more sympathetic towards him. She *had* told him she was sorry to hear it when L. C. told her his "mom" had cancer, but it did not alter her behavior really. At best, his announcement softened her attitude towards him, but that was about it. It had not caused her to run back to him begging for another chance, as he had fantasized that it might.

Then again, Kay had no idea what it was like not to have a mother. She had hers. Her own mother was always doting on her and on that spoiled brat Jason, acquiescing to their every whim. Neither Kay nor Jason had any idea what it was like to have your own mother go off partying and sleeping around when you were not even old enough to go to school yet; you were tossed out onto the street with nothing to eat and nowhere to go, while your father was only God knew where, pickling himself to death with liquor and beating them all when he did come home.

No, Kay had no clue. She had her mother, Catherine Miller; that busybody that always thought she knew what was best for everybody else. Catherine knew no more about loyalty than her daughter did. L. C. had just seen with his own eyes how loyal they both were to him. He seethed as he watched Kay, Catherine, and that tall, dark-haired man walk into the Blue Bay Seafood Restaurant to have dinner together on that Friday night when Kay should have been having dinner with L. C.

L. C. had not seen what the tall, dark-haired man was driving, or he would already have checked him out. He had been following Kay. He watched from a distance as she picked up her mother, and then he followed them to the Blue Bay. It was a seafood restaurant that sat in the middle of a shopping center, so it was easy just to park in a random spot and watch them.

L. C. was debating going into the restaurant and "accidentally" bumping into them when he saw that Catherine and Kay paused in front of the entrance as if they were waiting for someone. Then L. C. saw him. He watched as the man put his arms around Kay – *his* Kay – in a quick hug. Kay apparently was introducing the man to her mother, because they shook hands, smiling.

Waves of rage washed over L. C. But he had to get a grip on himself. He could not afford to cause another scene in a restaurant in Salisbury, not after the manager had called his fellow cops on him just days ago. It was that stunt, after all, that had resulted in his suspension from the Department. It was all Kay's fault. But he had to be smarter this time. He *was* smart. He just needed to stop and think, to plan. Until he came up with one, he would just watch.

He sat and waited until he could not sit still any longer. If Kay wanted to be unfaithful, then he could too. What he needed was a good distraction to calm him down and clear his mind so he could think. He thought of a woman named Shirley he had met at a shag dancing club a few months prior. He had hooked up with her a time or two, but she had really ticked him off when she told him that she had been out target shooting with some other man. He had reacted by making some "anonymous" calls to her as well, but mostly just hang-up calls to her house to find out if she was home or not. He did call her one night and just played the song "Stand By Me" on her voicemail recorder. He was certain that she had no idea that he was the caller. She needed to listen to that song, to learn what being loyal to a man meant.

In a particularly lonely moment back in October, he had called Shirley again, this time telling her that his mother in Ohio had been diagnosed with breast cancer and only had a year to live. He sounded pretty upset on the phone, even to himself. She was instantly sympathetic and came over right away. He practiced his sad, fictitious story on her. He told her that he and his mother were awfully close. He told her he worshiped the ground his mother walked on and he did not know if he could go on after she died. Shirley felt really bad for him and offered comfort as best she could. She had let him have his way with her that night, but he had not seen nor talked with her at all until just a couple of days ago, when he was not getting anywhere with Kay and needing some female companionship.

After sitting in the parking lot a few minutes longer, L. C. decided he could not waste any more time or Shirley would be at his house before he was, and he needed to take a shower. Oh, how he felt like he needed to shower. After just watching Kay let some other man put his hands on her, L. C. felt violated. Kay belonged to him and to him only. She was part of him. L. C. had to get home.

The shower did not make him feel much better. He had barely gotten dried off when he started perspiring again, just thinking about what he had seen at the Blue Bay. Where was Shirley anyway? It was two minutes before six, and she was supposed to meet him at his house at six o'clock. He despised people who could not be on time.

When Shirley arrived promptly at six, she found L. C. pacing in his backyard. He seemed nervous, agitated. They sat down on a bench for a moment to exchange greetings and to chat, but he popped right back up and asked her if she was ready to go. He could not sit still.

"Did you find that Robin Williams movie I wanted to see, *Mrs. Doubtfire?*" she asked him, and motioned to the newspaper she saw spread out on his patio table.

"Uh, no, I couldn't find it playing anywhere. Let's just go to dinner," he said.

"Oh. Okay," she replied.

L. C. had not looked for the movie, nor did he want to. He thought if they could get back to the restaurant in time, he might be able to get inside with Shirley and make Kay jealous. That would serve her right, he thought.

L. C. drove them through town in his Monte Carlo, through the parking lot of the shopping center and all the way around the Blue Bay, but Kay's car was gone. He slammed his fist hard on the dustless dash of his car. L. C. was unsure where to go next. He was so distracted with his thoughts that his driving became erratic. Shirley finally asked him what was wrong.

"My dog died," he said, speaking the first thing to came to mind.

"Oh no!" Shirley said, "What happened? He looked fine when I saw him just a few weeks ago!"

"Caught some virus," L. C. said, clearly dropping the subject. He needed to keep his stories straight, he thought to himself. Oh well, who was she going to talk with about his dog?

There was no sign of Kay's car in town. She had to have gone back home.

He drove into her subdivision. He stopped twice in town to use a payphone.

"Is anything else wrong?" Shirley asked him.

"No, just checking my messages," he said without further explanation.

"Where are we going?" Shirley asked, looking around curiously. L. C. had driven them into a residential neighborhood.

"Um, there's a house in here I am thinking about buying," he told her, and pointed out a brick ranch home that was not much larger, if at all, than his current home. Shirley saw one car parked outside the house at that time. They did not stop to look at the house. L. C. drove out of the subdivision and back into town. He finally stopped for dinner at Irving's Restaurant. They ordered chicken dinners, although L. C. was not hungry and did not eat much of his dinner.

L. C. needed to calm his nerves. He could tell he was making Shirley uneasy. She was asking too many questions. He downed a couple of beers. Maybe that would help. He wanted to calm down, yet he did not want to become impaired to the point that he could not think clearly.

"I can tell something else is bothering you," Shirley said. Why had he not just cancelled his date with Shirley? She was getting on his nerves, distracting him when he needed to be planning. He could have found out what Kay's date was driving. He could have run his plates and found out who he was, where he lived, all the information he would need to formulate a plan. But now he had tied himself down for at least a while longer tonight. Now he had to tell her something or she would just keep nagging him.

"I'm still upset about my mother," he finally told her.

"L. C., you are going to have to go back to Ohio and see her. She's sick," Shirley encouraged.

"Didn't I tell you?" L. C. asked.

"Tell me what?" Shirley responded.

"My mother died."

"I'm really sorry, L. C. I didn't know," she told him sympathetically.

"She died, and we buried her already. She had just gotten out of the hospital, and she just lost the will to live. We rushed her back to the hospital, but she died there."

Shirley was shocked that she had just been diagnosed with breast cancer and had died so quickly afterward. No wonder L. C. was not himself, she thought.

It was about 10:00 PM when they walked back into L. C.'s house. He was still hyped up. Finally, he asked her for a favor.

"Sure," she said agreeably. "What is it?"

"I have a friend whose wife is running around on him. He's trying to get custody of their children. Would you mind driving your car to my friend's house so I can take a look? I'd drive my car, but my car and my tag would be recognized."

"Why doesn't your friend hire a private investigator?" she asked. She asked too many questions. It was getting on L. C.'s nerves.

"He's a police officer. He can run tag numbers and easily get any information he needs."

At 10:15, Shirley drove L. C. in her car, following his directions. She found herself back in the same neighborhood they had been earlier, when L. C. said he was considering buying that brick ranch house.

"Do you have anything to write on?" L. C. asked her.

Shirley reached into the back seat where she kept some blank medical forms for work. L. C. pointed out to her the same house he had said he was considering buying. This time, however, the lights were on inside. Shirley pulled into the driveway, and L. C. freaked out.

"Back out! Back out!" he shouted at her. This woman was an idiot, he thought.

She couldn't back out immediately because there were two cars coming down the street.

"Back out anyway!" he shouted. She eased down the street and pulled back onto it as quickly as she could. L. C. was busy writing down the license plate number from the big boat of a car parked beside the house. It was a large, light-colored sedan.

When they were driving back down the street, L. C. seemed to calm down.

"Well, I guess that's their kids' car," he commented.

"The kids are old enough to drive and they're fighting for custody?" Shirley asked. She's not *that* big of an idiot, L. C. thought. He would have to think before he spoke. He did not want Shirley to know the brick ranch house actually belonged to Kay Weden.

He shrugged. "Well, he's trying anyway."

She drove them back to L. C.'s house and they went inside. L. C. went straight to his bedroom, and Shirley followed him. L. C. picked up the phone in his bedroom and began dialing. Shirley sat on the bed and listened. L. C. called a friend and asked him to research the license plate number. The friend called back a few minutes later. Shirley watched as L. C. wrote down the information he was given.

L. C. had what he needed, at least for the time being. He turned to Shirley.

"Wanna spend the night?" he asked her.

"No thanks, I had better get back home. I have to get up early in the morning."

L. C. walked Shirley to her car, gave her a quick hug, and kissed her goodnight. It was approximately 10:45 PM.

As Shirley drove out of sight, L. C. looked at the name he had scribbled in his bedroom. Viktor Ake Lennart Gunnarsson. What kind of foreign loser was that guy, anyway? He was probably an illegal, a bum. He wondered how in the world Kay got hooked up with him. On the internet again, probably, he thought. Stupid computers. He was not very computer savvy. In fact, he barely knew how to turn one on. He was much more comfortable with electric typewriters.

He had composed the vast majority of his "anonymous" notes and letters to Kay on the electronic typewriter at the high school where he worked as a School Resource Officer. One good thing about being suspended, he realized, was he did not have to be around all those goody two-shoes teachers and all the spoiled, smart-mouthed kids. He liked it when they admired him in his uniform and his badge, though. Some of the girls even flirted with him. He'd like to show them what it was like to be with a real man, he had imagined more than once. But mostly they just got on his nerves, watching how they came to school driving a car they never had to pay for, wearing new clothes and expensive athletic shoes, bragging about their vacations here and there with their families. They disgusted L. C.

He was not going to waste any more time. He had to formulate a plan and fast. He did not know if the Gunnarsson man was going to stay at Kay's all night, but he doubted it. He doubted it because Kay did not like to have overnight guests with her teenage son in the house.

L. C. decided to go check out the man's address. The new phone book displayed Gunnarsson's name and phone number and listed his current address as 910 Lakewood Apartments in Salisbury. He would go there, and he would definitely go alone. No one could be trusted. He had been a cop long enough to learn that.

He checked the Monte Carlo for anything that could be used against him as a weapon. He knew already that it was clean; it was *always* clean. He made sure of that on a daily basis. He did not think he had left anything lying on the rear seat, in the glove compartment, the console, or the side pockets of any of the passenger doors. He checked them anyway. Who knows what Shirley could have left inside? But when he checked, he found nothing other than the user manual that came with the car. He left it in the glove compartment along with a state map which may serve to be quite useful, especially since he could not exactly stop and ask anyone for directions.

Before leaving his house, he checked the items off the mental list he had created. Everything he needed was in his duffle bag except for his police uniform shirt which was still on its hanger. He carefully hung it on the hook behind the driver's seat. He could not stand a wrinkled uniform. Some of the rookies at the P.D. walked in at work looking like they had never seen an iron, much less knew how to use one properly, especially the ones who lived on their own with no mother to take proper care of their uniforms. More and more citizens seemed to be disrespecting cops, he had observed. Officers did not need to add to the disrespect by looking sloppy. He had no tolerance for a sloppy cop. He belittled them at every opportunity, hoping to shame them into doing better.

Belittling other people had always given him a rush, a sense of power and control in a world of precious little power and control for him to grasp. That injustice, however, was about to change. He checked the apartment number once more and committed it to memory. L. C. was fairly familiar with the complex location, although it had not been on his assigned beat when he was on patrol.

Lakewood Apartments was a large complex barely inside the city limits of Salisbury. It consisted of multiple buildings, and the street leading through them all just dead-ended. There was only one way in and one way out, although L. C. discovered that he could drive around several buildings and not be seen at others. He made several slow trips around the two-story, wood-framed buildings with their long, wooden-railed balconies across the front. He saw that none of the buildings had elevators. There was a set of exterior wooden stairs leading up each side of each building, leading to the second level of the apartments.

Gunnarsson's apartment was 910. L. C. spotted it fairly easily. It was on the second level of one of the older buildings at the back of the complex. All of those buildings faced the large parking lot. L. C. had hoped that Gunnarsson's apartment was on the ground level. It would have made it a lot easier for him to get him out and into L. C.'s car, rather than dragging him down the steep stairs, if it came to that.

L. C. parked his car near the opposite end of the parking lot, not too close to Gunnarsson's apartment, but close enough to see if he showed up and went inside. The lights inside the apartment were off, and the wooden door was closed, most likely locked. L. C. would just bide his time, watch, and wait. While he waited, he reached into the back seat and pulled his police uniform shirt from a hanger on a hook above the rear driver's side door. His badge was already pinned to his left chest pocket, but he had removed the brass nameplate from the right chest pocket before leaving his house.

He removed his heavy, dark green jacket and his nice pullover sweater, tossing them neatly onto the rear seat, and he put the uniform shirt over the short-sleeve t-shirt he was still wearing. He would have put the shirt on before he left his house, but he did not want to take the chance on running into one of Salisbury P.D.'s finest on the street wearing any part of his uniform while he was on suspension. He, in fact, did not want to draw attention to himself in any way until *he* was ready.

Now, however, it was time. L. C. wriggled around in the driver's seat until he got his shirt tucked into the waistband of his navy-blue dress slacks which he was still wearing from his date with Shirley. They were not uniform pants, but they would do in the dark. Most citizens were oblivious to details anyway, he had concluded a long time ago.

As it turned out, he did not have to wait for long. At around 11:30 PM, the same car

L. C. and Shirley had seen in Kay's driveway, the large, light-colored sedan, a Lincoln in fact, pulled into the complex. L. C. watched as the man he had seen at the Blue Bay Seafood Restaurant parked his car and walked up the flight of stairs to his apartment. It was the first apartment on the end. L. C. was glad that he would not have to pass by anyone else's apartment to get in or out of Viktor's apartment.

L. C. hated everything about him, from his ugly car to his ugly brown bomber jacket. He hated the confidence with which he walked. He tried not to think about the man being alone with Kay inside her house earlier that evening, but he could not help it. He had seen the light from the candles on her dresser glowing through her bedroom window. He knew the entire house well, from one end to the other, but he especially knew her bedroom. The thought of what had probably occurred in her bedroom tonight while he was passing by on the outside wrenched his guts into knots. He hated Kay tonight with a pure hatred, and he hated this Gunnarsson man too. But he was glad, in a twisted kind of way, for the hatred; it fueled his courage.

L. C. put his running Monte Carlo into gear and moved it from its current idle position to a parking space closer to Gunnarsson's car and closer to his apartment building. Better to get him out voluntarily, he thought. He stared at the car wondering what kind of person a man had to be to own such a ridiculous vehicle. He had not even parked it correctly; instead of parking directly in between the lines as they were clearly marked, Gunnarsson had parked the car diagonally, taking nearly two full parking spaces. *What a selfish, inconsiderate...* L. C. did not finish his own sentence, because he had made up his mind. The man would be nothing after tonight.

By dawn, Gunnarsson was unlikely to be able to bother anyone ever again. L. C. intended to make absolutely certain that Gunnarsson stayed away from Kay for good. It was already close to midnight, and he needed to get on with it. The big dumb car of Gunnarsson's had inspired L. C. with an idea for approaching Gunnarsson nonchalantly. It was time.

Looking around the parking lot for the umpteenth time, L. C. saw no movement around him. He rolled down the driver's door window, shut the car off, and listened. It was eerily quiet. Although a couple of cars had come and gone, no one was hanging around outside on the apartment balconies or in the parking lot. It was far too cold for that on this early December night. He turned the key just far enough to the right so he could roll up the driver's window. He felt for his weapon without looking down at it, the way he had been trained. He turned the ignition key to the left, removed it, opened the driver's door, locked the car, and stepped out.

L. C. put his car keys into his left front pants pocket. He did so in case his right hand was occupied when he needed to get back into his car. He pulled on the fitted, black leather driving gloves he had jammed into his rear pants pocket before he left the house, but he had another pair just like them in the console, under the roll of black electrical tape he had thrown in when he was unable to locate any duct tape. He could have sworn he had some duct tape but could not recall where he had put it because it was not in its usual spot in the cabinet inside his utility room.

After considering it for a few moments, he had arrived at the conclusion that the electrical tape was even better than duct tape because he had tested it. He had tried to tear it in two with his bare hands before leaving the house and had only succeeded in twisting it into wads he could not straighten back out. He cut the mangled piece from the roll and wiped his fingerprints off the smooth, flat surface all the way around before adding it to his supplies. He also threw in a roll of masking tape he spotted in the same cabinet, just in case, because he was not sure exactly how much electrical tape was still on the roll. Of course, he still had his cuffs, not the ones issued by the Salisbury Police Department, but some old ones he had acquired elsewhere.

L. C. had seen the light go out in what was apparently the living room of apartment 910. No matter; he wanted to catch the man off guard. Perhaps he had even gone to sleep already. L. C. knocked on the wooden door, mildly at first but then a little harder. He really did not want the neighbors to hear or to look out their windows at him. He shielded his face as best as he could from the direction of the security light in the parking lot. Then he heard footsteps.

They sounded like the bare footsteps of a man, as far as L. C. could tell.

"Coming, coming," a man called from inside the apartment. He had only spoken two words, but already L. C. could tell he had a foreign-sounding accent. He said the word "coming" as if it had a "k" on the end. L. C. stepped back and to the side of the door as he had been trained when he heard the man fiddling with the deadbolt lock and then the door handle. But as soon as he opened the door, L. C. moved forward and stepped inside before the man had a chance to step out of the apartment and onto the balcony.

He was taller than L. C. had anticipated, definitely over 6 feet tall, possibly a couple of inches over. L. C. resented the fact that at 5 feet 10 inches tall, he had to look upward to make eye contact with him. L. C. noticed that he was wearing black underwear, briefs, to be exact. But he had pulled on a terry cloth robe and was tying the belt as L. C. walked inside.

"Salisbury Police," L. C. said to the man. The skin on his chest was smooth and tan,

L. C. noticed, or possibly he was just dark complected.

"How may I help you?" the man said cheerily.

"Is that your Lincoln parked out there?" L. C. asked.

"Yes, it is. Is there a problem?"

L. C. ignored the question. "What's your name?" he asked the man. "Are you Gunnarsson?" he asked, only he pronounced the first syllable like "goon." It was a small dig, but it amused L. C.

"My name is Viktor Gunnarsson. What is the problem, Officer?"

"I'm gonna need you to step outside with me."

"I will just change my clothes quickly," Viktor said and turned towards his bedroom, but L. C. stopped him.

"Hold it right there!" L. C. commanded, and then a bit more calmly he added, "You're fine like you are. This will only take a minute. Stay where I can see you."

Viktor looked momentarily baffled, but he did as he was directed.

"May I put these shoes on before we step outside?" Viktor asked politely, pointing towards a pair of brown loafers he had left sitting by the front door.

"Go ahead," L. C. said, watching the man reach down for his shoes. He then took the opportunity to glance around the apartment. It was a mess of clutter. L. C. wondered why there was so much junk mail in piles on the floor and on the coffee table. Viktor's apartment was the complete and total opposite of L. C.'s home. It also reeked of a something pungent …*garlic,* that was what it was, apparently coming from the kitchen area. L. C. hated garlic. He hated the taste of it on a woman's mouth and the smell of it on a woman's breath. He would not kiss a woman with garlic on her breath, or any other unsavory odor, until she brushed her teeth, gargled mouthwash, or preferably both. Not unless he had to.

Viktor Gunnarsson had only said a few words to him, but he could see that Viktor's teeth were straight and white. His parents probably worked themselves to death to pay his orthodontal and dental bills growing up, L. C. thought distractedly. He had never even had a consultation with an orthodontist. Thankfully, his own teeth were naturally fairly straight, but no matter how much baking soda or hydrogen peroxide he used, his teeth were nowhere close to the dazzling white of Viktor Gunnarsson's.

When his shoes were on his sockless feet, L. C. told him to come on. Viktor Gunnarsson dutifully followed him out the door into the cold night air, wearing only his underwear, robe, and the slip-on shoes. L. C. walked out first, then stood to the side of the door waiting for Viktor to walk in front. Viktor stepped out the door of his apartment for the very last time. L. C. watched as he took the first step down the steps. It would be easy just to give him a hefty shove, but no, that was not what he had in mind.

CHAPTER FOURTEEN

**"How beautiful upon the mountains are
the feet of him that bringeth good tidings,
that publisheth peace..." (Isaiah 52:7)**

L. C. had always thought that his burgundy Monte Carlo resembled an unmarked police cruiser, and he liked that. It was, in part, the reason that he had bought it. He drove only American-made cars. He hated foreign cars almost as much as he hated foreign people.

"Is this your car here?" L. C. asked Viktor once they had walked down the steps and into the parking lot.

"Yes, sir, it is," Viktor answered. "I always park like this, kind of sideways. Is that the problem, sir? Because I can move it if you would like for me to."

L. C., however, did not answer his question. He was thinking.

Finally, he said, "It's too freaking cold to talk out here. I need you to get inside my car, in the front seat on the passenger side."

L. C. unlocked and opened the heavy passenger door, but as Viktor started to step inside, L. C. said, "Hold up just a minute. Put your hands on top of the car."

Viktor paused and turned to face L. C.

"I said put your hands on top of the car!" L. C.'s hand was on the grips of the gun on his belt.

Viktor did as he was told. L. C. reached up as he had done to a thousand individuals before and took hold of his right wrist, bringing it around and down to his lower back, roughly slapping one side of the hinge cuffs on with his left hand.

"Give me your other hand!" L. C. ordered firmly but quietly.

Viktor again complied. "Are you arresting me?"

"Get in the car, now." L. C. put his hand on top of Viktor's head and pushed him down into the seat. Viktor sat awkwardly in the front seat, his robe agape. L. C. reached across him with the seatbelt and snapped it into place. He looked down at the man's long legs, with his knees almost touching the glove compartment. L. C. could not care less about the man's comfort. In fact, he was about as comfortable as he was going to get.

Viktor adjusted his arms and hands as best he could with the cold metal cuffs closed too tightly on his wrists.

Viktor was confused. "Officer, what did I do? Why are you arresting me?"

L. C. closed the car door, swiftly walked around the front of the vehicle, opened the driver's door, and got behind the wheel. He inserted the key into the ignition and quickly locked the doors. He started the engine but kept the transmission in Park.

L. C. turned towards Viktor. The man was clearly uncomfortable, cold, and afraid. L. C. wanted to laugh at him but decided he would have less trouble if he kept up the charade for a little while longer.

"By department policy we have to handcuff anyone we transport."

"You aren't arresting me?"

"No, I'm not taking you to jail. I need to take you somewhere else, to show you something."

"Where are we going?" Viktor asked.

"You'll see when we get there," L. C. said.

"But I thought this matter was something about my car," Viktor said, confused.

"No more questions." L. C. said hatefully.

"But, sir…"

"I said no more questions. Now shut up!" L. C. ordered in raised voice.

Viktor was confused. He did not understand how American police officers worked, to be sure. He had never been in trouble in America. Still, he found this officer's behavior strange. He felt it was best to comply and wait and see where he took him. The officer clearly did not like being questioned.

When he cuffed him, L. C. had seen that Viktor was wearing a gold-colored watch and a gold signet ring on one finger. He considered only briefly that he might later take the watch and ring and sell it but dismissed the thought just as quickly. It was stupid things like that, that got people caught. No, he would not take the watch or the ring. He must remember to remove the cuffs after it was all over, however, because handcuffs have serial numbers on them, and he could not be sure that he had not been issued this older set from some department in the past where a record of them being issued to him could be found.

Assessing the present situation, L. C. could not believe how well it was going, how easily he had gotten Gunnarsson out of his apartment and into his vehicle. He had not even had to unholster his gun. He figured he would not be able to get him into the car except at gunpoint, but this stupid foreigner had done just exactly as he was told. L. C. found most people to be sheep.

This Viktor Gunnarsson, or whatever his name, was completely under L. C.'s control, and L. C. thrilled at the realization. He was so proud of himself, so sure of himself all of a sudden. Gunnarsson was shivering now from the cold and probably also from fear, L. C. observed.

L. C. drove out of the apartment complex and turned left, the opposite direction of town. Viktor squirmed uncomfortably.

"These handcuffs are pretty tight," he complained to L. C. "Could you loosen them a bit?"

L. C. did not answer.

"Sir?" Viktor began again.

"Where were you tonight?" L. C. demanded. "Where did you go?"

"Excuse me?" Viktor sounded confused.

"I asked you a question, and you're gonna answer it. I asked you where you were tonight, and you better tell me the truth!" L. C. was driving in a less populated, more rural area of the county.

"I, I went to dinner with a friend, and, and her mother. Then I just went to her house and visited. I don't understand why you..."

"A friend, huh?" L. C. snarled.

"My girlfriend, actually," Viktor said, unable to prevent his voice from trembling.

"Your girlfriend! *Your* girlfriend you say? She's not your girlfriend!" L. C. shouted at him.

"What?" Viktor said, growing more confused by the minute.

"What's her name?" L. C. asked. "What is her name?!" he shouted.

"Kay," Viktor said. "Kay Weden."

"And Kay Weden is my fiancé! Did she bother telling you that?" L. C. spat at him.

"No, sir. I didn't know that, sir. She told me she was not seeing anyone. Sir, I had no idea. Please take me home now."

"You aren't going anywhere till I say so!" L. C. shouted at Viktor, clearly enraged.

"If this is about Kay," Viktor began.

"Don't say her name. Don't say her name again!" L. C. snarled.

How dare he! How dare this man claim Kay as his girlfriend after all L. C. had done for her! After all the time he had listened to her mouth, after all the times he had made love to her, after all the promises they had made each other, promises which he expected her to keep!

"Did she tell you she was engaged to a cop?" L. C. asked Viktor.

"N-no. She didn't."

Bam! L. C. slammed the dash with his fist. He was struggling to maintain control.

The very next moment, he asked Viktor in a deadly calm voice, "What did you do to her? Did you go to bed with her? And don't you even think about lying because I already know everything!"

Viktor said nothing. He did not know how best to respond.

"I asked you a question!"

"I m-made love to her. But just this one time. Never before."

"At her house? In her bedroom? In her bed?" L. C. hated himself for asking, but he had to know. He just had to hear it for himself.

"Y-yes sir. But just this one time, sir. It was the first time," Viktor explained. "And I didn't know, I swear I didn't know she was your – that she was engaged to be married to someone, to you. I swear I didn't know!" Viktor was genuinely scared now, just like L. C. wanted him to be. Viktor needed to suffer. He had to pay the consequences for his actions. He had to be punished, and the penalty was death. There was no way around it. Viktor had to die. L. C. could not leave any loose ends. He could not let Viktor go, only to tell Kay what L. C. had done. He would lose her for sure then. Not that the thought of her with another man's semen in her was anything but revolting to L. C. Still, she belonged to him, not to some foreign-sounding…

"What kind of stupid foreigner are you, anyway? Where are you from and why are you here in the United States?" L. C. demanded.

"I am a native citizen of Sweden," Viktor responded. "Please, sir, just let me leave, and I will return to Sweden and never come back here again. I swear it!" he begged.

"Shut up!" L. C. shouted. "Just shut the h*ll up! If I want you to speak I will ask you something. Otherwise, I don't wanna hear a word you have to say, you sorry b*st*rd!"

"But I just…"

"D*mmit, if you don't shut up, I'll tape your mouth shut!"

Viktor forced himself to close his mouth and sit as still as possible. He could not believe what had just happened, and his current predicament. Fifteen minutes ago, he was in his bed falling asleep. Now he was in a terrible nightmare, and it looked as if he would not be able to talk his way out of it. His captor was wearing a gun, while he himself had no weapon of any kind. He barely had any clothes on. He glanced around the car, trying to see as much of it as he could with only the light from the car's dash panel for illumination. He saw nothing useful with which to protect himself, even if he had been able to free his hands. Both wrists were smarting painfully behind his back, but he was afraid to mention them again.

L. C. stared straight ahead out the windshield as he drove through the dark night, his senses on high alert. Adrenaline surged through his veins as anger pulsed through his body. He had suspected that Kay would sleep with the man, but now he knew for certain. He wanted to kill the man right then and there.

"How long have you been seeing Kay? And don't lie because I've been watching both of you."

"Not long at all. Just a few days."

"I said don't lie!"

"A week at most!" Viktor replied.

"How did you meet her? Tell me now!"

"Through a friend. A mutual friend, someone I used to date."

"Her name! Give me her name!"

"Tana! Her name is Tana!"

"I know that b*tch," L. C. said. He really did not know her, but Kay had mentioned her a few times. He had no use for any of Kay's so-called girlfriends. They were all a bunch of stupid wh*res.

"I know you met Catherine too. How did she like you sleeping around with her daughter?"

"I only just met Kay's mother tonight. I, I don't know what she thinks of me or Kay. She seemed nice is all I know," Viktor said, his voice trembling. He was crying now.

"Kay doesn't need you," L. C. told him bluntly. "She doesn't need a sniveling baby like you. You don't love her. You don't love her, do you? Do you!?"

Viktor was afraid to answer either way. "N- no sir!"

"So, you just used her then? You used her just to get your rocks off?"

There was no way to win, no matter what he said. Viktor was trying to tell L. C. whatever he wanted to hear, but it was hard. It was hard to know what that might be. Then he had an idea.

"Sir, can I pay you? Can I pay you for your trouble?" Viktor asked, desperately. He looked down at his robe. "I don't have any money on me, but my wallet is back in my apartment, and I have some money in the bank. I could…"

"I don't want your d*mn money!" L. C. spat. "You rich b*stards think you can just buy everybody and everything to get your way. I bet you really tried to impress Kay and her mama by buying them dinner tonight, didn't you? Isn't that what you thought?"

"I, I'm not rich. I, I, I didn't pay for dinner." Viktor hung his head down.

"Who paid for it then?" L. C. demanded.

"Um, well…"

"I asked you a question, you m*ther f*cker!"

"Kay's mother. Mrs. Miller did. She paid for all of us to have dinner."

"I'll bet she did!" L. C. said, his knuckles white on the steering wheel. "What the h*ll are you doing in America? Trying to freeload?"

Viktor was not sure what the term "freeload" meant. But he answered, "No, sir." Viktor's mind was reeling, but he could not think of anything to say that would not further infuriate this man. "Sir, may I ask what your name is?"

"That's none of your d*mn business!"

"I'm sorry. I just, I…"

"Shut up. Just shut up!" L. C. said, peering intently out both side windows of the car. Viktor thought he must be looking for something.

"Please, please let me go! I swear I will never go near her again! I didn't know she was engaged to be married to you! I didn't know! I'm not that kind of man to take another man's wife or girlfriend! I didn't know! And if you'll only let me go, I'll, I'll do whatever you say, I'll go wherever you tell me to, I'll…" Viktor could not help himself. He had to beg for his life; he could not stop. He had always been able to talk himself out of precarious situations. But this man was insane. He was crazed with anger.

"Shut up! Just shut up, I said!" L. C. slammed on the brakes and pulled off the shoulder of the road, and Viktor heard gravel hitting the car's undercarriage beneath him. Viktor looked around frantically, but all he could see was darkness and the shoulder of the road in front of them, illuminated by the headlights of the Monte Carlo. He had no idea where they were, but at some point, they had turned off the main highway and were on a paved street that did not have any visible white or yellow lines. Viktor fleetingly considered trying to get the car door open and run, but by the time he released his seatbelt with his hands cuffed behind him and then reached for the door lock and then the door handle, this crazed policeman would shoot him.

"I warned you to keep your mouth shut." L. C. killed the engine and, with it, the headlights. "Move and I'll kill you," he told Viktor.

L. C. reached into the duffle bag on the rear seat and felt for the roll of electrical tape.

Because he was wearing gloves, he couldn't get the tape started, but he was not about to remove the gloves. He reached into the bag again and removed a switchblade knife that he had seized from an arrestee months ago and never placed into evidence.

He pressed the button on the knife, and the blade shot forward. He used it to loosen the electrical tape from the roll and then placed the switchblade on the driver's door armrest without taking his eyes from Viktor. He then bound Viktor's hands together securely before removing the handcuffs.

"What are you doing? Please! Please, sir!" Viktor exclaimed.

"Shut up and don't move!" L. C. said through gritted teeth.

L. C. bolted out of his seat and out the door, unholstering his personal .22 caliber revolver as he did so. He pointed the gun at Viktor and kept it on him as he walked around the front of the car and opened the passenger door.

"Get out," L. C. told him firmly.

"But what, where…"

"I said get out. Get out now!"

"My seatbelt…"

L. C. reached across Viktor to hit the seatbelt release with his left hand. His face was so close that Viktor could smell the cop's aftershave. It was a strong musky odor. For a split second he thought about head-butting him, but he still had the gun in his right hand. Better wait for a better opportunity, Viktor thought. He did not want to die. He was too young to die. Wasn't he?

"Now walk to the back of the car," he ordered Viktor, "and don't try anything or I'll blow your head clean off your shoulders. Do you understand me?"

"Yes, sir," Viktor replied and walked slowly to the rear of the car. He was facing the trunk.

"Turn around." Viktor turned 180 degrees with his back to the car. He could see nothing in front of him but road. He prayed for a passing car, but there were none. He saw the outline of trees on either side of the road, the woods being considerably denser to his left. If he could run before the cop shot him, he maybe could hide in the trees…

"Lay down on your stomach," L. C. ordered. He was standing right beside him. Viktor fell down onto his knees on the hard ground. He didn't want to fall forward on his face, so he turned slightly sideways, trying to brace his fall on his right shoulder. L. C. kicked him in the back, and Viktor sucked in his breath at the sharp pain.

L. C. held the .22 caliber Dan Wesson revolver in his right hand, pointed downward in Viktor's direction as he walked to the driver's door and reached inside for the duffle bag. He sat it on the trunk of the car and looked down at Viktor Gunnarsson, this terrible man who had been with Kay just a few hours ago in the most intimate way a man can be with a woman. Kay was *his* woman. His! She loved *him,* not this stupid foreigner who readily admitted he didn't love her but had put his nasty hands and everything else on her, and inside her. L. C. kicked Viktor hard again, this time in the ribs, to release some of his anger. Viktor just whimpered like a whipped dog, with no fight in him, like Misty used to whimper when he kicked her around the house. Stupid dog! He was glad she was gone, and Viktor likewise would soon be only a bad memory.

Viktor's robe had pulled open when he got out of the car, and the only thing protecting him now from the cold ground was his flimsy black underwear and his shoes. It served him right, L. C. thought, not caring in the least if Viktor froze to death right there on the spot. Viktor's back and ribs throbbed where L. C. had kicked him in anger.

L. C. reminded himself he needed to be calm so he could think. This sorry excuse for a man wasn't worth going to prison for, no way. He had to be smart in the way he went about this. It never really occurred to him that what he was doing was wrong. What did "wrong" mean anyway? The world needed to be rid of people like this, this foreigner from Switzerland or Syria, or wherever the h*ll he was from. Such men just showed up here and had their way with American women like Kay. L. C. decided he was doing every American man a favor by getting rid of this loser.

Still wearing his tight-fitting leather driving gloves, L. C. managed to tape Viktor's feet together, in spite of the man's shaking. It was overcast and right around freezing at 34 degrees when L. C. had left his house on Lake Drive in Salisbury. It felt much colder than that now with the wind picking up.

He bent down beside Viktor's head and bound his head initially with the masking tape and then with the electrical tape on top of that. He wrapped the tape around his mouth and his eyes. He wished he had a rag or something to shove in Viktor's mouth, or perhaps a sock. But he was not going to give up one of his socks, and Viktor wasn't wearing any. The tape would have to suffice. L. C. left only Viktor's nose uncovered so he could breathe. L. C. did not want him to die right away, and definitely not in the trunk of his car. Although L. C. did not mind otherwise if he suffocated, he had seen plenty of D.O.A.'s and did not want any of Viktor's body fluids leaking out of his nose, mouth, or ears and onto L. C.'s car. Besides, L. C. preferred for Viktor to stay alive a little longer to agonize over what he had done. He wanted to terrorize this Viktor Gunnarsson. L. C. opened the trunk lid.

He bent down and took hold of Viktor's elbow.

"Get up!" he ordered, and tried to yank him off the ground, but Viktor was too heavy. Viktor rolled to his side and pulled his knees up, trying to assist in the process as best he could. His legs were numb from the ground, and he barely felt the raw skin on his knees. He finally got to his feet.

"Get in there," he directed, motioning inside the trunk.

Viktor's eyes grew even wider. He tried to speak, but his speech was muffled by the tape. Still, L. C. understood his useless protests. Viktor was begging. But L. C. shoved him face-first into the trunk with his legs hanging out the back.

"Get your legs in there or I'll cut them off with the trunk lid!" L. C. threatened. Then

L. C. remembered his police training, that a person "hog-tied" as Viktor now was, could easily suffocate in a matter of minutes if left on his stomach.

"Turn onto your side," L. C. ordered, and he pulled at Viktor's arm to assist.

Viktor turned to his side in the trunk and pulled his legs in with knees bent, almost to a fetal position. L. C. raised the gun to Viktor's temple. Viktor peered at the gun and at L. C.'s face with sheer terror in his eyes. L. C. felt in control, superior, and powerful. He enjoyed the feeling for a moment, and then replaced the gun in its holster.

"I hope it was worth it, you son of a b*tch!" L. C. remarked and closed the trunk lid with a slam.

The two-hour drive was excruciating for Viktor. He could not see anything at all and could hear very little. Breathing was difficult and labored, and he hoped his nose would not stop up from the cold, since he could not breath at all through his mouth. He kept working his mouth and jaws, until he finally worked the width of the tape into his mouth. He tried unsuccessfully to chew it in two, but he did work it into a sticky, narrower strip inside his mouth that allowed him to breathe through his mouth around it.

Several strands of tape covered his mouth, his eyes, and his ears. He tried working his hands loose, but he had lost feeling in his fingers because his tape bindings had cut off the circulation.

Viktor rolled to his stomach as best he could and tried kicking the trunk lid, but he could not get any power behind his kicks with his feet bound together. Perhaps he should have fought. He was bigger than the cop, but he had no weapon of any kind, and the cop did. He cried. He wanted to scream, tried to scream, but there was no one to hear him, and his mouth and throat were so very dry.

"Shut up back there or I'll shoot you through the backseat!" L. C. called to him.

Viktor quieted down. Then he thought of the spare tire and the tire tool. Surely the car had a spare and a changing kit somewhere in the trunk. He squirmed around until he could get his bound hands down under the flap that he was lying on. He wiggled to the side of the trunk as far as he could go and felt beneath the flap. He felt a hard rubber surface. There was a spare tire! That meant there was also a jack and a tire tool. He felt around with his hands behind his back for what seemed like an hour but all he could retrieve was a metal pin of some type, small and useless. The jack and tire tools must be underneath the spare, which he could not budge from his position.

Perhaps he could use the pin to unlatch the trunk lid. He tried and tried until he could no longer move his arms, but his efforts were futile. He squirmed around again until his feet were near the trunk latch. Though they were bound together, he rolled to his side again and tried to kick at the latch, accomplishing nothing. With the pin still in his hands, he tried to scratch at the sides of the trunk, but that seemed to serve no purpose either.

If only he could get the trunk lid open somehow, then he would have to be ready to jump out with the car moving and run like h*ll. He would roll in a somersault as he had seen stuntmen do on television when they jumped out of and away from a moving car. But no matter how he tried, nothing budged the lid. He had read that modern cars had an emergency release latch that could be activated from inside the trunk, but this was not a newer model car. It was probably not even a 1980 model. He searched in the dark for such a release but found none.

Perhaps it would be better to conserve his energy. His breathing was already shallow from the exertion, made worse by his ever-growing panic. He tried to rest, to calm down so he could think. But when he stopped moving a new fear washed over him, the fear of freezing to death. He could not be sure, but he felt as if they were climbing in altitude. He felt the urge to yawn but could not do so because of the bindings on his mouth. His ears were popping; yes, he was sure they were driving on an incline.

Viktor tried to think of where such a place could be. Relatively new to North Carolina, it was not as familiar to him as it should have been. He tried to think. There were no mountains around Salisbury that Viktor was aware of. The Appalachian Mountains were somewhere in northwestern North Carolina, but he had never been to the area, so he was not sure exactly how far away they were. He was not even sure of how long he had been riding in the trunk of the car, but it seemed like many, many hours.

Viktor thought of his parents, his sister, his family in Sweden. He had come to the United States not only seeking political asylum but seeking some relief for his family from the unrelenting harassment from the media in Sweden over the prime minister's assassination. He well remembered being arrested by the police in Sweden, but that had been completely different from the treatment he had received thus far from the American policeman. The Swedish Police had not been particularly friendly, but neither had they been cruel to him, as this terrible cop had been and was being still.

How very ironic, he thought. How ironic it was that he had been accused of such a treacherous crime against his native country, and that upon being released he would come halfway across the globe to the so-called land of the free, the land of opportunity and the promise of protection, only to end up in such an awful predicament all because of a woman he had basically just met.

He thought of Kay then, of their evenings spent during the past week, which may very well be the last week of his life. He thought of how they had made love – was it just a few hours ago? He could not be sure now. The cold was getting to him. His robe did nothing to warm him. He tried to lay close to the rear seat, hoping to absorb some heat from the car's interior, but it was of little comfort. He recalled with fondness the softness of Kay's worn mattress, the fresh feel of her sheets, and the floral aroma from her scented candles. He loved how Kay had felt in his arms and beneath him. He loved the taste of her kisses. He hoped such reminiscing would warm him, but they only warmed his heart. His body was growing colder and stiffer by the minute.

Viktor realized that he *had* fallen in love with Kay in the short amount of time that he had known her. She was educated, intelligent, intellectual, and fun. He loved her heartfelt laugh, and he especially loved how she laughed at his attempts at humor in particular. She was an optimist, and Viktor had always loved optimists. His time with her had simply flown by over the past several days and nights. Yet he did not think it advisable to admit to the cop how he really felt about Kay. He guessed that was not at all what the cop wanted to hear. Perhaps he had guessed incorrectly. Perhaps there was no correct answer.

Surely what his captor said was untrue. He could not possibly be engaged to marry Kay. Tana would have told him. *Kay* would have told him. Reminiscing over the past week, he recalled no indication whatsoever that she was seeing another man, much less engaged to be married. The policeman was most assuredly a disturbed man.

Viktor wished now that he had not admitted to sleeping with Kay, although regrets were futile at this point. What if the policeman went to Kay after he finished with Viktor? What if he attacked her, or worse, what if he kidnapped her in the same horrible way? What if he did something unthinkable to her because Viktor had run his mouth without thinking? Yet, the cop seemed to know everything. He said he had been following them both for the past week. Maybe Viktor had done the right thing by being honest; maybe he had not. He had no way of knowing for sure.

Viktor needed a plan of some kind, but as they continued to climb, Viktor felt as if he were losing the ability to think clearly. The cold had permeated his flesh to the bone. His arms and legs were aching with pain, and his muscles were spasming. He started squirming again, wriggling his head back and forth and grinding it in frustration on the carpeted trunk mat, a small concession of comfort for which he was thankful. At least he was not lying on bare metal. The trunk was far too small to stretch out his legs, but he longed to do it in the worst way. It was a small thing, the ability to move one's limbs freely, and yet he could not even do that. His fingers and hands were completely numb, as were his feet. He wondered idly how they could still be hurting so badly and be numb at the same time.

Viktor prayed, making more promises to God than he had ever made in his life. If only God would spare him from this cruel cop and this entire heinous nightmare, he would be a better man. He would do more for others. God was not a stranger to Viktor. He had always believed in God, and in Jesus, the Son of God. He believed that God loved mankind – including him – so much that He sent Jesus to this world to be crucified to pay the sin debt for all mankind, to all those who would accept His Son Jesus as Savior. Viktor had done that, and above all else, that was the most important thing. He was comforted by the fact that if this truly were his last day living upon this earth, and it sure was looking that way, he would wake in Heaven. He would see His Savior and he would thank Him for all the blessings of his life. He would not question his Lord's decision if it were his time to go.

With that thought and a prayer for Kay on his lips, Viktor closed his eyes under the tape bindings. The cold was not bothering him so much anymore, he noticed. He had stopped shivering. Now he was growing sleepier and sleepier by the minute.

Hypothermia can kill a human being in as few as thirty minutes. Cold temperature causes the body to lose heat rapidly. If a person is without the protection of shelter, strong wind can cause the body to lose heat at an even faster rate. The body loses heat faster than it can produce it. One who begins to shiver from the cold does so in order to maintain a friction type of heat from the rapid involuntary shaking of the muscles. Mild hypothermia begins to set in when the body's temperature drops only one or two degrees. Most people are familiar with this stage. Its symptoms are goose bumps on the skin, numbness in the fingers, toes, nose and ears, and slight shivering.

As hypothermia continues to worsen, the human body is unable to increase its own temperature without assistance. Shivering becomes more severe, the skin becomes colder, and one begins to suffer other adverse effects such as disorientation, balance difficulties, and poor judgment. Medical attention is required. Brain function becomes appreciably impaired. More severe symptoms include a drastically slowed pulse rate, a marked shallowness of breathing, extreme sleepiness, and eventual loss of consciousness. Finally, death occurs.

Viktor knew little of hypothermia other than the fact that it generally meant freezing to death, but now it occurred to him that he was experiencing it firsthand. He had advanced to a peaceful state where sleep was knocking at the door. He had only to slip into it as easily as one would slip beneath the surface of a warm blue pool, sinking slowly into its comforting depth. Viktor felt himself slipping even now. Perhaps he would wake in Heaven and never even have to look on the face of the cruel cop again.

Brusquely, however, a bitter wind brushed over his still body. The car was stopped, he realized. The Monte Carlo's trunk lid was open, and the cop was jerking at his robe, yelling something angrily at him. It sounded jumbled to Viktor, who was still in a semi-conscious state. He tried to move his legs and found them to be unresponsive to his will. He closed his eyes again.

L. C. had reached his destination. It was dark, but the sky was clear, and there was just enough light from the moon so that L. C. did not have to use his flashlight. When he pulled off onto the side of the Blue Ridge Parkway next to the wooded mountainside, he had pulled on his heavy, green insulated jacket with the deep pockets over his police uniform shirt. He was still wearing the black driving gloves and had no intention of removing them. From one of the deep jacket pockets of the coat he removed a black wool toboggan and stretched it over his head. It was well into the lower twenties here in the mountains, but L. C. did not intend to stay out in the freezing cold for very long.

He had driven the last several miles in peace and quiet. Viktor Gunnarsson, if that was his real name, had stopped thrashing around in the trunk. L. C., glad for the quiet so he could think and mentally rehearse his plan, also hoped that his captee had not suffocated or frozen to death. He did not want to have to haul his overgrown body into the woods. He wanted the pleasure of killing this man to be his and his alone. The man deserved to suffer. L. C. sadistically hoped his appendages were frostbitten though, the fingers that had touched Kay in places where he had no right, and not just his fingers. Looking down at him, L. C. was not sure Viktor was conscious.

L. C. reached into the trunk and shook his passenger violently. Viktor groaned and moved slightly, and L. C. could see that he was still alive, though in much worse shape apparently than when L. C. had shoved him in the trunk a couple of hours prior. He seemed to be disoriented.

"I said get out!" he ordered, and Viktor started moving, albeit with the speed of molasses.

"I, my, my legs, they are so stiff," Viktor groaned.

"I don't give a sh*t! I said get out now!"

"I, I'm trying." L. C. saw that Viktor had somehow slipped the tape that had gagged his mouth down below his lower lip.

"Try harder!" L. C. demanded.

Viktor rolled to his back and tried to scoot forward on his buttocks. L. C. impatiently reached in with his left hand and grabbed the taped bindings between his ankles. He jerked his feet out the trunk opening and pulled. Viktor slid forward and then slowly rolled over onto his stomach. He wriggled back and forth, trying to move himself backward so that he could plant his feet on solid ground. Then perhaps he could stand.

L. C. was growing more and more impatient. Gunnarsson was not moving fast enough to suit him. If someone drove by, the situation would deteriorate rapidly. He did not want anyone else involved; no witnesses, no additional victims in the wrong place at the wrong time. He just wanted to get this over with and get back on the road again... with no passengers.

After some struggling by both men to get Viktor up and out of the trunk, Viktor was at last on his feet. They were still bound together about the ankles, so his steps were tiny. L. C. was walking behind him and giving directions, poking him in the back with the barrel of the revolver with every tiny step Viktor took. The ground was uneven leading into the dark woods that were thick with age old pines and pin oaks. Viktor tripped and pitched forward.

"I can't get up! I can't walk!" Viktor cried.

"Then crawl! Just get moving, d*mn you!" L. C. ordered. "I don't have all night."

Viktor tried walking on his knees, but with his hands and feet still bound together he could do little more than scoot a few inches at a time. Finally, L. C. told him to stop moving, and he took out the switchblade. He reached down to cut the tape between Viktor's feet.

"So help me, if you so much as make a single move I don't command you to, I will blow your head off right here!"

"Thank you, sir, thank you." Viktor made several awkward attempts before finally getting back to his feet. L. C. was no more than three feet behind him, and the gun was pointed directly at Viktor's head. Viktor considered his options. Should he just break loose and try to run? But his feet were still numb. His legs felt like rubber bands. Surely, *surely* he could somehow reason with the officer when they reached their destination. Perhaps he had calmed down on the drive to wherever this place was, and he would not kill him. Why then was he marching him to such a secluded area? Viktor's brain seemed scrambled. He could not seem to follow a train of logical thoughts to a reasonable conclusion.

With each step they took further and further into the woods, all vestiges of hope were vanishing into the thin mountain air. Viktor's eyes were still covered by the tape bindings, but he discovered that he could see beneath the bottom of the tape if he looked straight down at his unbound feet. Pine needles, black dirt, and protruding roots were all he saw. He bumped into several trees, one or two of them with considerable force even at his slow rate of movement. He smelled pine as the woods became thicker.

L. C. walked behind Viktor, careful not to trip on a root or in a hole, but simultaneously scanning the landscape for an ideal location, far enough from the road to delay discovery – possibly until springtime or even later – but not so far that he would have a long way to walk back, carrying the items he would need to take away with him. He would know the right spot when he saw it.

Suddenly, there it was: a fallen pine tree. The wind must have blown it over at some point in the not-so-recent past, pulling the root ball up and out of the soft earth which was now frozen as hard as rock. It was an ideal place to leave a dead body and easy to find, should he have a need to return at some point in the future, though he certainly hoped not.

"That's far enough!" L. C. told him. "Stop right there."

Viktor stopped and nearly fell forward from the dizziness he was experiencing but was somehow able to remain standing. He realized with finality that there was nothing here, nothing to see. He had been brought here for one reason, and only one reason. He wanted to beg, to plead for his life, but all he could manage was, "Please..." He was exhausted, disoriented, and devoid of strength, but he had to try something.

He could almost feel the cop's breath on the back of his neck; he was so close, only an arm's length away. He could also hear him directly behind him. If Viktor was ever going to make a move to save his own life, he had to do it now. With one sudden motion, he turned and tried to kick the cop as hard as he could. Sadly, all he felt was air; he had not made contact. He had misjudged his position, and he nearly fell down again. The cop was laughing at him, laughing... demonically. Despite his laughter, the cop was even more angry.

Although Viktor may have surprised him temporarily, L. C. saw that he was weak.

His attempt to fight him both infuriated and amused L. C. Now he was just plain sick of this sniveling, whining man who was, as far as L. C. was concerned, a trespasser in this country. Worst of all, he had trespassed against Kay, against L. C.'s property, so to speak. She belonged with him and no one else. They would be together soon, and Viktor Gunnarsson would receive no forgiveness for his trespasses.

Viktor turned to face the cop, his hands still bound behind his back. Viktor threw his head backward to see as much as he could beneath the tape, and it was then that Viktor met his captor's eyes in one final, silent plea. In his captor's eyes, two identical bottomless pits of blackness, Viktor found only vile; no pity, no compassion, no mercy.

"You should have stayed wherever the h*ll you came from. You will *never* touch Kay or any other woman ever again, you son of a b*tch!" L. C. informed him icily. "I hope you burn in h*ll!"

The last thing Viktor saw on this side of eternity was the cop extend his right hand, the hand that held the gun. He turned his head sharply to the left just as L. C. was exerting approximately eight pounds of pressure on the trigger of the .22 caliber Dan Wesson revolver. The round struck Viktor on the right side of his neck and did not exit. He fell immediately onto the ground, onto his side. Blood did not escape right away. For a moment there was only a small hole, barely visible on his neck in the moonlight as L. C. watched without remorse. Then it darkened. Blood began seeping thickly from the entrance wound. Viktor's legs were twitching.

L. C. took a step closer towards him, kicked at him, and then with his foot, pushed Viktor over onto his back. His legs were still moving. L. C. leaned forward and, taking better aim at closer range, he fired another round just to be sure, striking Viktor in the left temple. Viktor lay motionless on the cold ground, his robe twisted about beneath his body.

It was done, but L. C. could not leave; not just yet. He would have to remove the bindings next. He knew enough about trace evidence to know that hair and fibers and who knows what else would stick to the adhesive on the back of the tape. He was not about to leave that on the scene just in case the hillbilly cops around here knew a clue when they saw it and knew what to do with it if they did. That was in the unlikely event that they ever found the body. Looking around at the desolate, wooded nightscape, L. C. doubted anyone would even find the body before it became completely skeletonized. He was pleased overall with the location.

Using the switchblade to remove the tape bindings took only a matter of seconds. Then L. C. quickly stripped the body of his shoes, robe, and underwear, careful to avoid getting any blood on himself. He wadded the tape, clothing, and shoes into a single ball, and with one last effort, he pushed on the man's shoulders until he had him shoved underneath the protruding roots of the fallen pine. L. C. left Viktor Gunnarsson to finish bleeding on the cold ground, lying flat on his back, his eyes partially open yet not seeing the overhanging tree branches or the clear night sky above them. There now. As L. C. saw it, the chance of his body being spotted was slim to none, and slim was out of town.

What L. C. did not see in the dark of the night was the one piece of binding that had fallen from his arms and onto the ground at the victim's feet. It was approximately eighteen inches long and consisted of both masking and electrical tape. It was covered in blood droplets, black hair, and had one noticeable .22 caliber hole on one end. The length of tape would remain at Viktor Gunnarsson's feet for the next 35 days.

CHAPTER FIFTEEN

**"One witness shall not rise up against a man
for any iniquity, or for any sin, in any sin that
he sinneth: at the mouth of two witnesses, or at
the mouth of three witnesses, shall the matter
be established." (Deuteronomy 19:15)**

Lisa sat back down at the table after her restroom break,
across from Don and Terry, awaiting their next questions.

"Did L. C. – Excuse me – *Lamont* ever tell you why he
chose to drive to the mountains, to Deep Gap, as opposed to
another location?" Don asked her.

"He told me that before he killed Viktor, when he and Kay
were still together, he took Kay to the mountains, you know,
to Watauga County. He kind of knew his way around there, I
guess. He said he drove Viktor to some road in Deep Gap on
the Blue Ridge Parkway. When he stopped, he said he made
Viktor get out of the trunk and marched him down a bank
and then back up a hill I think, and then when he thought
he had him far enough into the woods, he shot Viktor two
times, once in the neck and the other in the head after he
fell down. Lamont said his hands were shaking, and then his
hands shook just the same way when he killed Mrs. Miller."

"Do you know what kind of weapon Lamont used to
shoot Viktor Gunnarsson?" Don asked. Two .22 caliber
rounds were recovered from Viktor's body at the autopsy.
We learned that one of the gun possibilities was a Dan
Wesson revolver, which L. C. happened to own, but had

seemingly disappeared off the face of the earth following the two homicides.

"He said it was a .22," Lisa answered.

"Do you know what kind of .22?"

"I – I'm not sure," she said as she looked away.

"Did he tell you what he did with either or both of the guns?" Don asked.

"Yeah. He said he took them with him to South Carolina. To Charleston. He went there with Wanda-somebody right after he killed Mrs. Miller, or at least that's what he told me."

"He did go to South Carolina. Now, let's go back to when Lamont said he killed Viktor in the woods in Deep Gap... what did he tell you he did after that?" Terry asked.

"Well, he said it was in the early morning hours by the time he got back to Salisbury. But he did say he stopped somewhere on his way back to wipe the trunk of his car out. He also told me that after that, maybe the next day, he took his car to a car wash and had the trunk area cleaned out, like professionally." It was Sam's Car Wash, and L. C. had stood over the car wash employees, instructing them when they did not clean to his satisfaction. One employee in particular recalled L. C.'s visit specifically because L. C.'s demands were so much out of the ordinary. L. C. required the employee to vacuum, shampoo, and vacuum again the carpeted trunk mat of the Monte Carlo.

Don and Terry had a few more questions for Lisa Collins before they had to return to Salisbury. But this was not to be the last time they would question Lisa.

After Don and Terry shared Lisa's statement with me, I imagined as I had so many times before, Viktor being in his apartment ready for a good night's sleep when L. C. Underwood knocked on his door. What if Viktor had simply refused to come to the door? What if he had spent the entire night with Kay at her house? What if Rick had refused to run the license plate number for L. C? What if Shirley Twitty had spent the night with L. C.? Would L. C have changed his mind somehow? Would Viktor be alive today? Would L. C. have gone on to kill Catherine? Or would it all just have delayed the inevitable?

All of those things *did* occur, however. Perhaps it was a perfect storm. Viktor did answer the door and he did comply with what he understood to be a legitimate police matter. But L. C. Underwood was not in the process of executing his police duties when he did any of the things he did on the night of December 3, 1993, regardless of the fact that he was wearing a police uniform, his issued badge, and his non-issued, personally-owned .22-caliber handgun.

Terry called me again the following week.

"Are you going back to talk to Lisa again soon?" I asked Terry.

"Yes. We're heading back down there next Thursday. Wanna come?" he offered.

"I'd love to. But y'all have a good rapport going with her right now. I'm not about to mess that up. Besides, I'm slammed here. I have a bunch of break-ins, a rape of a college student, and a horrible child molestation case I'm in the middle of investigating... and that's just the new cases that have been added to my already massive caseload," I griped.

"I know what you mean. But child molesters – I hate them. I know you're not supposed to hate people, but I swear I hate them. And I hate working those cases."

"Typically, very little in the way of physical evidence."

"Right. And no eyewitnesses."

"What those monsters have done to some of these children..." he trailed off. He had seen as much or even more cruelty than I had.

"Right. Well, H*ll's getting hotter all the time."

"No doubt," he agreed.

"About Lisa..." I said.

"Yeah. Next Thursday, the eighteenth."

"Y'all go ahead. Just keep me posted please."

"Absolutely. Good luck on your caseload. Get the pervert."

"I'll do my best. Y'all be safe, and have a good day if you can," I said.

"Just another day in Paradise," he replied as he hung up.

Terry and Don returned to Fountain Correctional as planned on March 18, 1999.

"I remembered a few more things I forgot to tell y'all before," Lisa began.

"Okay then."

"Yeah, some things I remembered about Catherine's murder," Lisa stated. "L. C. went back there again."

"What do you mean, he went back there again?" Terry asked.

"After he killed her. He left, but then he went back about twenty minutes or so later."

"Why? Why did he say he went back?" Don asked.

"To put a long brown hair of Jason's in her hand. He said he also left some beer in her refrigerator, that kind that Jason drank, and a half of one sitting inside the house somewhere."

"Did he say what kind of beer that was?" Don asked.

"I think he said either Miller or Milwaukee beer." Neither Terry nor Don recalled any beer containers in the Miller crime scene, nor any hair found on Catherine Miller's body. L. C. may have conjured those things up later to impress Lisa with how smart he was.

"And did he tell you the purpose of the hair and the beer?" Don asked.

"Yeah, to make the cops think Jason did it."

"Kay's son Jason."

"Yes. Kay's son."

"Okay. What else?"

"I remembered some more about the guns. Ya know I told you that Lamont went to Charleston, South Carolina right after he killed Catherine Miller? Well, he told me he took both murder weapons with him. He put them in the trunk of his car, but he didn't say which car he drove, whether it was his Monte Carlo or that Dodge. Anyway, he said he threw one of the guns – I don't know which one – into this place in Charleston called The Battery, into the water. It's a place where ships come into port, so the water is really deep there. Lamont said he was by himself when he did that. He said he threw the other one into the water over one of those big bridges that connects Charleston to the mainland."

"When exactly did Lamont tell you that?" Don asked.

"He told me all of that before he ever went to trial," Lisa said, "in Watauga… But I'm not sure he was telling the truth about the guns," she amended.

Over not only the next couple of hours but also the days that followed, Lisa had even more to share. At Lamont's urging, Lisa informed Don and Terry that she actually moved to the state of Ohio to live with the family Lamont referred to as *his* family. Then in June of 1998, she and Lamont's "mother," Barbara "Bobbie," flew to Wilmington, on the North Carolina coast, to meet with Lisa's probation officer. The two of them also went to Eastern Correctional to visit Lamont in prison. Bobbie talked with L. C. in Lisa's presence for a while, but then Bobbie left Lisa to speak with L. C. privately.

"It may have been that day. I'm not sure when it was exactly," Lisa said, "but during one of my visits to the prison, Lamont told me he had not actually thrown the murder weapons in the water in South Carolina, but that he still had them, in a way. And it wasn't just the guns he used to kill Viktor Gunnarsson and Catherine Miller, either. He also had the .22 he used to shoot into Jason's bedroom window…you know, Kay's son."

"Are you saying he also confessed to you that he shot into Jason Weden's bedroom window?" Terry asked her.

"Yes, with a .22 long gun. …But it was the .38 that y'all want. That's the gun he wanted me to get for him."

"What do you mean, he wanted you to get it for him?"

"Well, first, Lamont told me that he had gotten the gun from Lincoln County. You know, when he worked at the Sheriff's Department there. He said he turned it back in, and they documented that, but then he went back and got the gun, so there was no new record that he had it."

"You are talking about the .38?"

"Yes, it was a .38 Colt Detective Special revolver."

"And did you find the gun? Did you get the gun for him?"

"No. I never touched it. But he wanted me to get it and throw it in the dam there."

"Where did he tell you the gun was located?"

"It's buried in the back yard of a house in Westerville, Ohio, where Burl and Barbara Childress live."

Upon request, Lisa drew a sketch of the property and marked an "X" in front of a tree where she believes the gun is located.

"And that's the gun he used to murder Catherine Miller?' Terry asked.

"I believe so, yes, although he told me that it wasn't. He said if y'all found that .38 you would use it against him anyway. But I believe that's the gun he used to murder Mrs. Miller."

"And did you look for the gun?" Don asked.

"Yes. I flew back with Bobbie – *Barbara* – from Wilmington, North Carolina to Ohio."

"You were living with the Childresses in Ohio then?"

"Yes, if you can call it that."

"What do you mean?"

"I'd rather leave it in the past. It was one of the worst times of my life, and I don't want to talk about it."

"What exactly did Lamont tell you to do with the gun?" Don asked.

"Well, he was extremely nervous. He was sweating. He probably wasn't sure if he could trust me or not. But he finally told me that the .38 was in a green plastic garbage bag, and that's where I found it. I dug it up, but I did not even pull the bag out. I didn't touch the gun."

"Why dig it up if you weren't going to get it?"

"I guess I just wanted to know if it was really there or not."

"What did you do then?"

"I covered it up with potting soil and some sticks and things. Then I put a salt block over it."

"A salt block?"

"Yeah. You know, like for cattle."

"Right. What about the other guns?" Terry asked.

"I'm getting to that. He told me I would find the .22 rifle inside the Childress' old house on Judson Road. He wanted me to find it and take it to the house in Westerville where they were living then."

"And did you do that?"

"Yes. I found the rifle in a closet in a back bedroom in the house on Judson Road where some of their family was living. I took the rifle back to the Westerville house. I laid it behind the dresser in the bedroom where I was staying."

"And the .22 rifle was…?"

"The one he used to shoot into Jason's bedroom window."

"What about the other .22? The one he used to murder Viktor Gunnarsson?" Terry asked.

"I don't know," she said, looking away as she answered.

"Lisa, are you willing to take a trip up there with us, to show us where you last saw the guns?"

She sat back in her chair and studied them, as if she were weighing her decision.

"Sure," she answered. "Why not."

The following week, Terry called me again.

"How was your vacay in the Buckeye State?" I joked.

"A total bust," he said, "and not in a good way."

"I take it you did not come back from Ohio with more guns than you took with you?"

"No. We searched high and low, hither and yon."

"I can't say I'm terribly surprised."

"Me either. But we had to try."

"Of course."

"So, what's the deal with Lisa?"

"Don and I think she may have been just wanting to get back at L. C.'s pseudo-mom for the credit card thing. They tried to make her life difficult, so…"

"Revenge. That's always a solid motive."

"True."

"Was she difficult on the trip?" I asked.

"Not really. I think she aggravated the female guard that accompanied us to some degree, perhaps, but she didn't try any funny business or anything…other than taking us on a wild goose chase, that is."

"I guess y'all are done with Lisa now?"

"Yes, at least I hope we are. Even if she was willing to testify to what L. C. told her about killing Viktor and Catherine, any shred of credibility she may have had is utterly destroyed."

"How's Don?" I asked.

"Not very happy at the moment, to put it mildly."

"I can imagine."

"Don talked to Kenerly, but we both knew what he was gonna say beforehand."

"Right."

"I guess we're back to square one," he said.

"I'm sorry, Terry," I said, and meant it.

"I am too," he said. "Lisa was probably our best chance for prosecuting L. C."

"Well, she was apparently able to accomplish something no one else has, and that's getting him to talk about the murders," I commented.

"She said he wouldn't shut up talking about them," Terry said.

"It's ironic, isn't it, Terry?"

"What is?"

"That with all of his malice towards women, he let one get close enough to burn him."

"I guess we have to give her that much credit, anyway," he agreed. "But she blew it."

CHAPTER SIXTEEN

"Why callest thou me good? there is none good but one, that is, God." (Mark 10:18)

As time passed and the seasons changed dramatically as they did in the Appalachian Mountains, L. C. Underwood occupied fewer and fewer of my conscious thoughts. Then suddenly, something pertaining to him would pop up out of the blue, and there he would be again, front and center in my life somehow. In late 1999, something completely unexpected occurred. I received a letter from a television producer who wanted to feature the Gunnarsson murder on a series entitled *The New Detectives: Case Studies in Forensic Science*. *The New Detectives* was a true crime show that had aired on Court TV since 1996. It not only aired in the United States, but internationally as well on the Discovery Channel UK, Discovery Europe, the Crime & Investigation Network in Australia, Prime TV in New Zealand, TV Norge, TV Denmark, Kanal 5 in Sweden, and RTL in the Netherlands.

The film crew arrived a few weeks later, following several phone conversations between the producers and Sheriff Lyons, Steve Wilson, and myself.

"Are you nervous about your big television debut?" Steve asked, teasing me.

"No, I'm not," I answered honestly. "Are you?"

"No," he answered, not completely honest. He seemed to be perspiring, I noticed, as he straightened the knot of his necktie yet again.

Sheriff Lyons looked cool and professional as always.

"Now, there is no need to be nervous," the film crew manager instructed me as I prepared for my first interview. "The good thing about filming is if you mess up, we can always go back and do a retake. We need to check some levels, color balancing and all that first. So, if you would, just say a few words, talk about anything…" The huge black camera was only a couple of feet away, occupying a large proportion of my forward vision.

"Hello out there in TV Land! My name is Paula May, and I am here to ask you a very important question. Do you suffer from occasional irregularity?" I asked, looking directly into the camera lens. Steve snickered, and Sheriff Lyons shook his head, trying not to laugh.

"No need to worry about her freezing up, Jim," the camera operator said to the crew manager, "she's not afraid of the camera."

We filmed reenactments, rehearsed statements for interviews, and several clips of us working in the Sheriff's Office. Then we drove to Deep Gap and trekked through the woods where Viktor Gunnarsson's body was found. Deputy Pat Baker, one of the first officers to respond to the scene in January of 1993, also accompanied us for the filming. He walked with me back to the spot where Viktor died.

"I don't suppose you believe in ghosts, do you?" he asked me.

"Just the Holy Ghost," I replied.

"I don't believe in ghosts either," he said, "but I'm scared of them though." We laughed.

"I'm not superstitious," I countered. "But I'm a little stitious though." Pat paused and then laughed as he got the joke.

There was no snow on the ground at the time of filming, so some of the effect was lost. Overall, though, the producers did a good job of telling the facts of the case accurately.

They focused primarily on the forensic evidence – Viktor's head hairs found on the carpeted mat of L. C.'s car trunk.

As they packed up to leave the Sheriff's Office the following day, they told me it would be a couple of months at least before the episode would be finished and another couple of months after that before it aired on television.

"When should I expect offers to start arriving from Hollywood?" I teased the producer. "You know, once I am discovered and all that?"

I imagine he had been asked that question a time or two.

"Don't call us; we'll call you," he said, grinning. I never received so much as an invitation to audition for a laxative commercial. After the episode aired, however, I did receive several copies of it on DVD, including one that contained all of the clips they filmed, including the bloopers and the rejected clips, not only the ones that aired. I thought that was neat of them to send those. It was a unique opportunity, and I figured that, except for the local news, it would be my first and last appearance on a television series, a neat little one-time thing in an overall career of good versus evil.

As I watched the first public airing in my living room with family and friends who had decided to make a celebration of it, a "watch party," as it were, I could not fully enjoy the lighthearted atmosphere, not as I should have. I kept wondering if there was another watch party of sorts occurring inside a penitentiary elsewhere in the state. I wondered if L. C. was watching the episode as well. I did not doubt that he knew about it because every local and regional newspaper had at least some mention of the case being featured on *The New Detectives*. He would surely have read about it, and if he had not seen it directly, then someone would have informed him.

After we had watched and critiqued the show, the intense atmosphere dissipated, and everyone's moods turned light once again. My eyes traveled around the room. My close friends and family were there.

I smiled on the outside, but uneasiness churned inside me. Maybe the TV thing was not a good idea after all. Maybe it would only further infuriate L. C. and stir him up against me all over again. Even worse, what if he did something to one of these people I dearly loved. I could not imagine losing any of my friends or family at the hand of L. C. Underwood or anyone with whom he might conspire.

No matter what happened, I could depend on them to support me when I needed it, to celebrate victories with me, to love me. I realized that I was very blessed. I thought of Kay and hoped that she and Jason had mended their relationship, and that they were surrounded by supportive friends as well.

I talked to Kay the day after *The New Detectives* episode aired.

"Why was the episode called *For Love or Money?*" she asked me.

"I have no idea. I didn't know they were going to call it that," I told her. It really was nothing about money. "I suppose they were talking about the motive for Viktor's murder, you know, when we found his body. Whether the motive was robbery or a love interest. I really don't know; I'm just guessing."

"What if it makes L. C. angry?" Kay said, verbalizing the thoughts I kept having.

"He's always angry," I told her. I did not want to fuel her fears.

"I know," she said, and oh, how well she did know.

CHAPTER SEVENTEEN

**"Many days and years shall ye be
troubled, ye careless women:
for the vintage shall fail, the gathering
shall not come." (Isaiah 32:10)**

Lisa

Since the trip to Ohio was fruitless, Don and Terry were both fairly fed up with Lisa. She had destroyed what remaining credibility she had, as far as Bill Kenerly was concerned. He did not believe that he could ever use her as a star witness – or any kind of witness now – in a murder trial of L. C. Underwood. Don and Terry's communications with Lisa came to an abrupt halt. Kay, on the other hand, was not about to let her disappear so easily.

Don and Terry had kept Kay loosely informed about L. C.'s jailhouse girlfriend, so she knew that L. C. had allegedly told Lisa about killing Kay's mother. But Kay was still having a difficult time moving past her mother's murder, especially since Bill Kenerly was still refusing to prosecute L. C. for murdering Catherine. Regardless of Kenerly's decision, Kay experienced an overwhelming need to know whatever details Lisa claimed to know.

I was not available to field her questions just then. I was completing the F.B.I. National Academy training, having been fortunate enough to be selected to attend the 204th Session in Quantico, Virginia. The leadership training lasted ten weeks, and although I came home to spend most weekends with my family, I was pretty much out of touch from January through March of 2001.

Kay believed the best way to obtain information about L. C. would be to question Lisa herself. She felt as if she had to meet Lisa and talk with her directly. Both Don and Terry advised Kay against contacting Lisa directly, and while it was probably unwise and not anything she was looking forward to doing, she called Lisa shortly after Lisa was released from prison. After a few lengthy phone conversations, Lisa agreed to meet Kay at a motel in the western part of the state. I did not learn of the meeting until after the fact, a deliberate decision Kay made. She well knew I would be upset with her for putting herself in such a dangerous position.

Kay was wise enough, at least, to take a friend with her. Liz, a good friend of Kay's from graduate school, was someone that Kay had confided in at length, and she was more than willing to accompany Kay to meet Lisa. Neither Kay nor Liz took with them any type of defensive weapon, not that they necessarily had reason to believe that Lisa was a violent person. But knowing how manipulative L. C. could be and considering the possibility that he and Lisa were close again, who knew what terrible deed he might have persuaded Lisa to perform. It certainly would not be the first time he had gotten someone else to do his dirty work.

"Kay, I have to ask. What were you thinking?" I chided her after the fact.

"I know it wasn't the smartest thing to do," she admitted. "But I just had to meet Lisa. I had to talk to her face to face."

"I just worry about your safety. Anything could have happened," I said, a little gentler.

"I realize that."

"It could have been a setup."

"Well, it was my idea actually, not Lisa's."

"She could have told L. C., and he could have made it into a setup, an ambush."

"I suppose so. But there was also the fact that she was married to someone else."

"Completely irrelevant where L. C. is concerned," I countered.

"Granted."

"Why did you feel the need to meet her in person, Kay?"

"I think it was a mutual psychological need. We had several phone conversations prior to meeting, so it wasn't that we needed to exchange information so much as it was just to see each other, to have a frame of reference."

"But if she's remarried, has a new life and all that..."

"I know better than anyone how L. C. Underwood gets under your skin, like a terrible disease, and just stays there. It's like he permeates your life for good, no matter how much you don't want him to. Even though she's married to someone else, I don't know that she isn't still in contact with L. C. In fact, I think she still is, at least on some kind of basis, even if it is just friendship."

"It's hard for anyone to be *friends* with L. C."

"Don't I know it. I tried to be just his friend. It's all or nothing with him."

"Or both," I said wryly.

"Or both," she agreed.

"Okay, I've lectured you enough already, but please don't ever, ever do anything like that again on your own."

"I won't," she promised.

"Alright then. Now tell me everything."

Lisa had already checked in and was waiting in a motel room in Maggie Valley, North Carolina, a couple of hours southwest of Boone, when Kay and Liz arrived. Lisa had rented a Chrysler Sebring convertible after having planned already to drive alone, without her husband, to the mountains and visit with her mother who lived in the area. Kay wondered why Lisa's husband was not with her and also why Lisa had not planned to stay at her mother's home after driving all the way across the state, but opted not to ask about either fact.

Kay knocked on the door of the room, and Lisa answered quickly. Lisa, dressed in jeans and a long sleeve, light blue cotton blouse, did not look at all like someone who had recently been released from prison. To Kay, Lisa appeared healthy and well-kempt. She could see why L. C. would have been attracted to her.

After introductions were made, Lisa invited Kay and Liz to have a seat. They sat in two brown chairs that matched the room's drab décor. Lisa sat on the bed next to her open suitcase.

Before they even got past all of the small talk, Lisa reached into her suitcase and nonchalantly took out a gun.

Kay and Liz involuntarily held their breaths with eyes wide as Lisa laid the gun on the bed beside her and resumed conversation as if she had done nothing out of the ordinary. Kay stared as the gun. She later recalled that it was silver colored, a revolver. She could not distinguish the caliber or make of the gun, but she believed that Lisa wanted her to see it. Could it have been the .38 caliber Colt Detective Special that L. C. had used to murder her mother? Kay could not help but wonder. Liz did not know what to make of the situation either. Her initial thought was that Lisa was just making a point of preparing to protect herself in the event Kay had a devious purpose for wanting to meet. Only later did she consider the possibility that Lisa was letting them know she had the murder weapon. Perhaps even, in some sick and twisted way, Lisa got some kind of gratification from putting it there in Kay's presence.

The gun lay on the bed, in the open throughout the entire visit, which lasted no more than thirty minutes. The gun was pointed towards the wall, not directly towards Kay or Liz, but its presence was ominous and impossible to ignore, though no one mentioned it.

"What did you talk about?" I asked Kay.

"Honestly, nothing of any substance. We had already covered everything that there was to discuss on the phone. Mostly we discussed our current situations and the fact that L. C. had been moved again to another prison, this time closer to Salisbury. It was awkward. All three of us were uncomfortable, so we cut the visit short."

"When it was all said and done, are you glad you went?" I asked.

"Um, no. In the end, it was not the right thing to have done. It was nothing more than a satisfying of my curiosity, and hers too, I suppose."

"Except that she had a gun. Never mind the fact that she was a convicted felon."

"Yes, there was that."

.When the four of us – Don, Terry, Steve, and I – mulled over what Kay had done, we were all on the same page. More than anything else, we were relieved that no one had gotten hurt. We also collectively agreed that, in all likelihood, Lisa and L. C. had resumed their relationship, at least in some form. Additionally, we were equally intrigued about the gun Lisa had displayed in Kay's presence.

CHAPTER EIGHTEEN

**"My destiny no longer has me conquering
the highest towers in the world,
but rather the void they protect.
This cannot be measured."
(Philippe Petit)**

As we had predicted, Lisa Collins and L. C. Underwood had resumed their romantic, albeit dysfunctional, relationship and were in regular communication with each other once again. She later explained that, at some point after the Ohio debacle, L. C. had changed his mind about trying to pin the credit card frauds on her. I wondered at the possibility of a bit of blackmailing having transpired or some type of exchanges of threats, but perhaps pursuing the accusations was just more trouble than it was worth for L. C. and Bobbie. In any case, as much as was practically possible, Lisa and L. C. reconciled.

The relationship L. C. and Lisa shared was tumultuous, as the vast majority of his relationships with women, including Kay, had been. At times, she seemed to hate L. C. as much as she loved him. L. C.'s emotions were much the same. Sometimes, I thought, that kind of love and hate are two horns on the same goat. Lisa later admitted that the "love" she felt for L. C. was fierce but unnatural, driving but aberrant. For each of them, no good was likely to come of it. A distinct void existed in the relationship that trust should have occupied.

Their communications were filled with jealous passion, possessiveness, and petulant accusation. Instead of driving them apart, however, these seemed to fuel their need to maintain each other's role in their lives, not unlike an addiction. Lisa was familiar with addictions and battled them in addition to her other demons. Her life at that point was a sad commentary on the loss of what Don and I in particular recognized as tremendous potential in an individual. She was a smart cookie, but her life had spiraled dreadfully out of control. She was in and out of trouble, her life problems exacerbated by her increasing dependence on pharmaceutical drugs.

A few months after Kay's visit with Lisa, Don Gale and a female detective working for the Rowan County Sheriff's Office by the name of Tonya Rusher left the city of Salisbury on a bright and sunny Tuesday morning. They were headed to the town of Mount Holly, North Carolina. Tonya Rusher was an experienced and capable investigator with a sharp mind and a fit, athletic frame. She shared the same last name as our District Attorney, Tom Rusher, but they were not related. Detective Rusher was quite familiar with the Catherine Miller case and had worked closely with Detective Terry Agner on a number of other criminal cases. Terry suggested that having a female go with Don to meet Lisa Collins at her home was a prudent idea, and Don agreed. Tonya was more than willing to help.

Don and Terry continued to keep me informed, and I was pleased that Lisa was again so willing to cooperate even though she might be playing games. Playing games was Lisa's *modus operandi* so to speak. I cheered Don and Tonya on from my office in the Watauga County Sheriff's Office in Boone and prayed that God would grant them success in their endeavor. Short of that, any further attempt at finding new evidence in the Miller case was strictly up to the investigators in Rowan County. My day would be busier than usual with even greater priorities.

As Don drove southwest in his state-issued car, his conversation with Tonya was interrupted by an alarming radio announcement. One of the Twin Towers of the World Trade Center had just been struck by a commercial airplane. A few moments later, the second tower was hit, alerting the world that an act of terror had been deliberately committed against the United States of America. It was September 11, 2001.

"God, help us," Tonya exclaimed, "New York is under attack!"

As they listened, they both realized the disaster was one of epic proportions.

"The body count in those buildings is going to be unbelievable," Don said. "Hundreds. No, thousands, I would say."

"And how awful for their families that are watching it all," Tonya said, "and just think of all the responding officers and firefighters and EMS personnel. It has to be a strategic nightmare – the ops, the communications, and the coordination required to manage that kind of disaster..."

As they continued traveling, taking phone calls, and listening to news broadcasts and the first law enforcement updates, they learned more about the events of that terrible morning and discussed the possibilities behind it.

"They better start looking for Osama Bin Laden," Don commented in his matter-of-fact manner.

"Ya think?" Tonya asked.

"I sure do," Don replied.

"I wouldn't be surprised," agreed Tonya, as they neared their destination. It was time to deal with the matter at hand, the purpose for their visit.

As Don double-checked the directions he had been given, his brow creased.

"What's the matter?" Tonya asked him.

"You're not going to believe this," Don said as he pulled into a parking space and turned to look at Tonya.

"Try me."

Don looked at the structure that had once been a single residence, but was later made into two apartments, not exactly a duplex but similar.

"What is it, Don?" Tonya asked.

"I used to live here."

"In Mount Holly?"

"No. Yes. I mean I used to live right here, in this very building. In fact, I lived in the same apartment Lisa Collins is living in now." Don was frowning and perhaps a mite shaken.

"What? When? When did you live here?" Tonya asked, confused.

"When I first started working for the SBI. I was a narcotics officer, and I was stationed here. I rented the very same apartment that Lisa Collins lives in."

"Wow. That's freaky," Tonya commented.

"No kidding."

Lisa answered the door. Suntanned, with shoulder-length blonde hair and blue eyes, she was not unattractive, but she did appear older than her actual years. She had a tough demeanor about her but also seemed somehow wary. Lisa, by that point, had had much experience with the criminal justice system. She had multiple convictions for fraud – obtaining property by false pretenses, worthless checks, and financial crimes. But Don and Tonya were not interested in those crimes. They were hoping that she could provide something of evidentiary value that could be used to prove that L. C. Underwood murdered Kay's mother Catherine Miller.

Don weighed the possibility that Kay would eventually fall apart, concerned that she might actually have a nervous breakdown. She was worrying herself sick with every move L. C. made, albeit from behind bars, and while Viktor Gunnarsson's family had gotten some degree of justice with L. C.'s conviction in Viktor's case, Kay could not. Hopefully, though, L. C.'s latest girlfriend could help to change that fact.

Don had shared with me that Lisa had remarried, but that marriage was failing or had failed, and Lisa was anticipating a separation in the near future. She had resumed, or possibly even maintained, a congenial relationship with L. C. and willingly shared that fact with both her husband and with Don.

Lisa answered the door on the first knock and invited Don and Tonya inside. Don was familiar with the layout of the apartment. Being back inside the apartment produced a strange sensation in Don as he glanced around. The apartment had actually changed only nominally, he observed. The wall color had not been changed, but it was more cluttered than he kept it, at least as he recalled. But to Don it was almost as if he had walked back in time. The investigations involving L. C. Underwood were filled with such strange occurrences, or coincidences.

Don quickly brushed aside his thoughts and the strange feeling brought about by being in the same apartment he had lived in so long ago, to get on with the business at hand. As he considered that, Tonya began.

"Lisa, do you think L. C. would tell you again in detail what happened when he went to see Catherine Miller on December 8 of 1993?"

"I think he will. I mean, he's already told me about it, so there's no reason why he wouldn't now. It's been a long time since he told me. He's already told me a lot. When we were in jail at the same time at Watauga, his cell was across the hall from mine. We talked about it a lot. We talked about everything. He told me about killing Kay's mama, and he told me he killed the Swedish man too."

"Viktor Gunnarsson."

"Yes, Viktor Gunnarsson."

"Then wouldn't he be suspicious if you brought it up and asked him to tell you about it again?" Tonya asked.

"Not if I tell him that I need him to help me deal with it so I can continue our relationship. He will do whatever I ask if he thinks I'm gonna leave him."

"Well, Lisa, I'd say L. C. Underwood has met his match."

"He's got nobody else really."

"So, you think he trusts you enough to talk about it again in detail?"

"I know that he wants a life with me. He will tell me."

"What do you mean by that exactly? Is that how you plan to get him talking?"

"I mean that when I tell him I have to know the truth before I can marry him, he will tell me."

"He knows you are married?"

"Oh yes, he knows. I told him my marriage is basically over."

"And are you confident that he believes you?"

"Oh yeah. Sure he does."

"Lisa, are you willing to wear a recorder and give it a try?"

"Sure."

"Why would you do that, Lisa?" Don asked.

"It wasn't right what he did, killing a little old lady like that. It was, it – it's uncalled for."

"Lisa, surely you understand up front that L. C. is a dangerous man. If or when he ever finds out you recorded him basically confessing to murdering Catherine Miller, he will hate you. You could likely become the subject of his anger, possibly even a target. We already know what he is capable of. Have you thought about that, Lisa?"

"I have given it a lot of thought. I'm no rat; I guess y'all have figured that out. But this is totally different. It's absolutely the right thing to do. I really am trying to do better, to get a handle on my life. I do have regret and remorse for the things I have done to people in the past. I sincerely want to help you guys. Any man who would do what Lamont did to an innocent elderly lady like Catherine Miller needs to pay for it. He needs to face up to what he did."

"Alright then. If you're sure."

"I'm sure. Let's do it," Lisa said.

Don loaned a digital recorder to Lisa, and for the next three months, she engaged L. C. in phone conversations when he was allowed. Each inmate in North Carolina is allowed up to 300 minutes per month, no more than fifteen minutes in any given day, to talk on the phone. Lisa provided to Don recordings of her conversations with L. C., but when she would ask him specifics about either the Gunnarsson or Miller murder, he clammed up. He told her he would not discuss the cases over the phone. He did say, however, that he would answer any remaining questions she had in person. He wanted to see her; he *needed* to see her.

Painfully obvious in the conversations was the fact that L. C.'s hatred of both Don and me had only intensified over the years. My fear of L. C. Underwood had never left. As his first parole hearing loomed closer and closer in the future, I felt my fears resurfacing. I simultaneously did and did not wish to hear what L. C. might impart in person to Lisa. But I did need to know, as did Don.

In the first few days of December, Don, Terry, and their supervisors discussed the risks involved in taking Lisa to visit L. C., and they promised to let me know what they decided soon. When Don called me toward the end of that week, I assumed it was to fill me in on the plans concerning Lisa Collins. However, Don was calling to tell me that he had just received a phone call from a defense attorney who had some disturbing news that only added to our concerns. The attorney's client was a fellow inmate of L. C.'s at the Pasquotank Penitentiary, who had since become a close personal friend of L. C.'s in prison. The client allegedly told the attorney that

L. C. was going to pay or possibly had already paid someone "on the outside" to "kill one, and possibly more, of the cops that put him in prison." The client was trying to obtain additional details from L. C. Underwood, but he wanted something in return for his efforts. The "something" was a reduction of the sentence the client was serving. He claimed the basic information he had voluntarily provided was out of good conscience; anything more would cost something. No deals were agreed upon, and no additional information was forthcoming.

Christmas and New Year's came and went without incident, although all four of us, plus Tom Rusher and Jerry Wilson, remained on guard and alert as we spent time at home with our respective families over the holidays.

"Are you willing to drive with us to Elizabeth City to visit L. C.?" Don asked Lisa shortly after New Year's. Don explained that he would provide the transportation and get her approved in the prison for a visit, but she would be visiting L. C. alone.

"Sure. Why not?" Lisa responded.

"And wear a wire?"

"No problem," she said.

"Do you want to discuss it first with your husband?" Don asked.

"Nope."

"Alright then. Let's do it."

"Let's do it," Lisa repeated.

CHAPTER NINETEEN

**"For nothing is secret, that shall not be
made manifest; neither any thing hid, that
shall not be known and come abroad."
(Luke 8:17)**

On Sunday, January 13, 2002, Lisa stepped up to the challenge.

AGENT DON GALE: The time by my watch is 1:37 PM. I just activated a Sony microcassette recorder and wired microphone being worn by Lisa Collins for the purpose of recording a conversation between Collins and prison inmate Lamont Underwood. This recorder is being worn with the permission of Lisa Collins. Lisa, is that correct?

"Yes, it is."

The conversation between Lisa and L. C. that followed was summarized to me by Don.

"So, did he confess on tape?" I asked.

"Well, yes, sort of," Don said.

"Don, what do you mean *sort of*?"

"Well… Lisa asked him questions, and L. C. answered them to some degree, but the quality of the recording is not particularly good. The visiting area was one large room. A lot of people were talking at once, and the room had a bad echo. But you can still hear some of what was being said on the wire, although you can hear Lisa a lot better than you could hear L.C."

"Is it clear enough to use as evidence?" I asked.

"I think so, but again, that will be up to Bill (Kenerly)."

"Does he know about it yet?"

"I am planning to go see him tomorrow and play the recording for him," Don said.

"How did Lisa do?"

"She did great. She did get him to admit to being at Catherine's, and to getting really mad. But he lied."

"About what?" I asked.

"He said he went there to ask her to pay him back the money that Jason broke into his house and stole from him."

"Jason never broke into his house nor stole any money from him."

"Exactly. I don't know if we can call it a confession when everything else he says is a lie and we can prove that it is a lie. A defense attorney will eat us alive on that, or try to anyway."

I sighed. "What did L. C. say happened then?"

"Well, basically, from what I could understand, he said he lost his temper and just snapped."

"Did he say specifically that he shot her?" I asked.

"That's hard to say," Don said.

"Can I listen to the tape?" I asked.

"Let me see if I can play some of it over the phone for you now…" Don tried to play the recorder into the phone, but I could not hear anything but muffled voices.

"I can't understand it. Can I just get a copy then, at some point?" I asked.

"Sure. But after Kenerly hears it, I'd like to get it to the lab and see if the analysts can do anything to clear it up." Again, Don tried to play me some of the conversation over the phone, but I could not hear anything except muffled voices.

"You're going to try to see if the lab can eliminate some of that background noise?"

"Yes."

"Well, keep me informed."

"You know I will."

Don sent me a copy of his summary of the recorded conversation between L. C. and Lisa, but it had not yet been transcribed. I would wait to see if the S.B.I. crime lab could clear up the recording and then obtain a copy from Don.

A few days later, Don called me again.

"How did it go with Kenerly?" I asked.

"Not well."

"What do you mean?" I asked, already anticipating what he was going to say next.

"He doesn't want to indict L. C. in the Miller case. He doesn't want to use Lisa or the tape recording."

"Please tell me you're kidding."

"I'm not kidding."

"He feels like we would blow our one shot at L. C. on this one thing, and he doesn't think the tape is clear enough for jurors to understand it all."

"Hmm."

"In addition, he thinks it might even be a problem to get Lisa in front of a jury because of her credibility issues."

"I can't see how that has anything to do with it. The recording speaks for itself. It should stand alone."

"Yeah, well…" Don said. "He is also maintaining his original argument that since L C. is securely behind bars, we ought not take a chance on getting his conviction in the Gunnarsson case overturned."

"He keeps on appealing. That could happen anyway," I reminded him.

"I know. But so far, it hasn't happened."

Whether the direct result of divine intervention or simply good old-fashioned police work and sound prosecution methods, each appeal effort L. C. had made to that point had ultimately failed. But each appeal, each move of L. C., set Kay on edge, and it seemed as if the appeals never ceased, and neither, as all evidence would indicate, did his fantasies of killing.

L. C. had made it abundantly clear that he not only hated Tom Rusher, Don Gale, and me, he also wanted us to die, to be brutally murdered. As for Kay, I do not think he necessarily wanted her to die, but he did want her to suffer relentlessly, even more so than she had already. If he had known the extent to which he was still making her suffer, how he had robbed her of a normal life, he would have been ecstatic with his narcissistic self.

Regarding Tom Rusher and me, L. C. had actually formulated plans to make us suffer as well, and ultimately to be killed. Tom Rusher received the first notice of L. C.'s evil intentions by, of all things, a facsimile. The fax was dated February 26, 2002, and it was from the Conference of District Attorneys and addressed directly to Tom. The President of the Conference of District Attorneys sent the fax along with an explanation that the State Bureau of Investigation had received information directly from an inmate who was incarcerated in the same prison with L. C. Underwood. The inmate stated that L. C. had already taken some steps to have the District Attorney of Watauga County murdered. The inmate said the District Attorney's name was James Thomas Rusher.

Threats were not new to Tom, but this specific threat had uncharacteristically unnerved him, just as L. C.'s threats against me had unnerved me as well. In addition to being notified of the threat, Tom was given suggestions for his own safety. Those suggestions included Tom varying his daily routines and habits, creating and maintaining a journal of his daily encounters, and so forth. The S. B. I. sent in an undercover officer as an inmate to try to befriend L. C., on the off-chance that he would confide in him any information in reference to the threats against Tom Rusher and against me. Not surprisingly, L. C. was suspicious of new inmates, though, and did not take the bait.

I knew instinctively that while L. C. hated Tom Rusher, it was unlikely to be with the same intensity that he abhorred me. I believed that one of the reasons was that I was a female whom he had not been able to control or manipulate to his advantage, though he had certainly tried. While I tried never to let on in his presence that I was afraid of him, the simple truth was that he terrified me.

Although I knew it was extremely unlikely, I kept telling myself that L. C. would one day forget about me, or that his hatred would lose its intensity over time. Instead, I was reminded over and over again that his hatred for me only deepened with time.

One such time, I was caught by surprise during an interview of a man I was questioning about a completely unrelated case – a theft ring that focused on stealing tractors and other pieces of heavy equipment and taking them to chop-shops in neighboring states for resale. The man had been in and out of prison, and had served time at one of the same penitentiaries as L. C. He had little to say about the theft ring, but he did have something else he wanted to talk about with me.

"I bet I know about as much about you as you know about me," he said out of the blue.

"Excuse me?" I said.

"I said I know a lot about you. Well – let me back up. I have *heard* a lot about you."

"Like what?" I asked, not really even mildly curious.

"Your husband Randy is a probation officer, ain't he?" he said.

Ah, that must be what he meant. I bet he was assigned to Randy on probation or parole. Randy and I often dealt with the same individuals in our professions.

"So, you know Randy?" I asked.

"Not really," he said.

I looked up from my notepad and met the man's eyes. I was tired, not in the mood to play games. "I don't understand then," I said.

"Y'all have a kid, a little girl I think."

Instantly all of my senses were on hyper-alert.

"Why don't you just say whatever it is you have to say," I told him carefully.

"I'm not trying to threaten you or anything, ma'am," he said.

"Then what *are* you trying to say?" I persisted.

"Like I said, I'm not trying to threaten you or your little girl or nobody. But I know somebody that is."

"Go on," I said, not taking my eyes off him.

"A guy you got for murder. An ex-cop."

"What about him?"

"Aren't you the detective that put him in prison?"

"He got himself put into prison. He killed at least two people in cold blood. I investigated the case along with some other investigators."

"He killed that Swedish man, or wherever he was from. Kidnapped him too, or something."

"Yes." I felt myself becoming impatient.

"I was in the yard with him at the same time, and we had meals together in the common."

"When?"

"Last year," he said.

"I'm listening," I said.

"Now, you're probably gonna get upset when I tell you this."

"I said I'm listening."

"…but I think you ought to know. Lord knows I ain't no saint. I been mixed up in some sh*t, pardon my language, that I had no business being in. But I ain't never killed nobody, and I don't believe in messing with a man's family – or a lady's family."

I waited.

"But he was talking to somebody about his case, and it caught my attention when he started talking about Boone and Deep Gap, and all because that's where I'm from, right?"

"Okay."

"Anyway, that dude Underwood, he really hates you. Said y'all set him up for a murder he didn't commit, and all the usual stuff men say in prison. Anyway, he blames you for his being where he is, locked up."

"He blames his problems on lots of people other than himself," I replied.

"I don't doubt what you're saying, ma'am, but I heard him talking to another inmate – I think they stay on the same cell block, but I'm not positive about that. But the ex-cop said he had someone check out where you live, your house, or something."

"Did he say who that was – a friend, or who?"

"I don't think he said."

"He said he *already* had someone check out my house or he was planning to?"

"I think he said he already had because he knows you have gas heat."

"What about the heat?"

"He has some kind of plan to blow up your house with you and your husband and your little girl in it. I don't know if you got any more kids or not. All he mentioned was a little girl."

I thought about that for a few moments.

"And how did he say he would accomplish that?" I asked.

"He didn't say, as far as what he would technically do, but he did say he was gonna hire or was in the process of hiring somebody to do it."

"Why are you telling me now?" I asked.

"I didn't want it on my conscious, especially a little kid."

"Then why didn't you tell me sooner?"

"I guess I should have. Did he do something already?" he asked.

"No."

"But the other man said nobody in the mountains has natural gas, which was what I was thinking."

"That's correct. There are no natural gas pipelines."

I did not tell this man that Randy and I did heat our home with propane gas. We also had a gas cook stove, gas logs, and a gas-powered hot water heater that were all powered by propane.

"...But then he said y'all have propane, and that propane's way more dangerous even than natural gas." I did not know if that was true or not, but he had my full attention.

"Why is that?" I asked.

"Well, for one thing, propane's heavier."

I waited for him to go on.

"Propane is heavier than the air. It hangs lower, settles to the ground when it leaks, or to the floor inside a house. Natural gas kind of just goes up into the air like a vapor that disappears. It scatters in the air, ya know? But propane is more apt to exploding. It doesn't evaporate into the air like natural gas."

"That still doesn't explain how he was going to cause an explosion, or how he intends to ignite something in the house," I pointed out. "Not to mention getting inside my house."

"Oh," he said, "getting in somebody's house ain't no problem." He was probably speaking from experience, and I knew that much was true.

"Look, ma'am, I didn't hear all the details, but I heard enough to know he had given it some thought. He said all he had to do was cause a leak and let the air-to-gas ratio get to a certain level, and then one spark would do it."

"Any idea when he was planning to do such a thing or when it was supposed to happen?"

"He just said it'd have to be done in the evening, or at night when y'all got home from work."

I pictured all of us in the living room after dinner, chatting, playing with Katie, or just watching TV. It was no longer just the three of us. I wondered if L. C. knew that as well. My paternal grandmother, who had lived across the road from me for most of my life, had experienced a significant decline in her health in recent months, so Randy and I had moved her in with us. Granny would spend the days in her own house with a wonderful lady hired to help with her lunch and minor housekeeping chores, and I would take her to our house when I came home from work in the evenings. If I had to work late, Randy would pick her up. I imagined the improbability of all or any of us escaping from the house if L. C. genuinely wanted to destroy my family.

I thought of a typical evening, and how Katie liked to climb up next to me on the sofa after dinner and cover us both with her purple, Barney the Dinosaur blanket. I pictured us saying our prayers beside her bed and reading to her as she quickly fell asleep. Katie was no longer a small child and was an excellent reader, but she still wanted me to read aloud to her at bedtime and I complied, knowing that one day she would no longer want me to hang out with her in her bedroom.

Naturally, I also thought of Beth Richardson and her daughter, and of how L. C. had tried to kill them both by turning on her gas stove while she was at work. He had just waited for her to walk in and light her cigarette as she had always done. But for the grace of God that prevented her from lighting that cigarette that day, both Beth and her daughter would only be memories now.

I felt sick, and it must have showed.

"Are you alright, ma'am?" he asked. "I just felt like I should tell you."

"Yes, of course. I'm fine. I wish you had told me sooner but thank you for telling me now."

L. C.'s plan to kill Beth and her daughter in a gas explosion at their home had failed. Yet clearly, he had not given up on the concept. In all likelihood, he had studied his failure and was perfecting a method to carry out his evil plan against me and my family, paying someone I would not even recognize, suspect, or ever even see to do it for him... someone who could get it right. I told Randy that night, but he tended to keep his feelings to himself. He did not want to talk a lot about it, but I could tell it was on his mind. We decided not to worry other family members about it, but just asked our neighbors to keep an eye on the house and let us know if they saw any strange vehicles around when we were not home.

In spite of the investigation that followed by state agents and other investigators from within and outside the Correctional system who explored the allegations, no formal criminal charges were brought against L. C. Underwood for conspiring to kill my family and me or to kill Tom Rusher. L. C. did, however, face some internal discipline including time spent in solitary confinement. Although I was assured time and again that L. C. would be closely monitored and that his efforts to hurt any one of us had been thwarted, I knew the terrifying reality was that as long as he was determined to do such a horrible thing to us, he could find a way to make it happen. No prison bars in the world could prevent it. I prayed for protection for all of us.

L. C. had the financial means to make almost anything happen. In addition to a healthy savings account and a lump sum payout from the Salisbury Police Department for his accrued comp time and vacation leave, for all of the months prior to his conviction he continued to receive pension and disability benefits. His home was paid for, so he had no ongoing mortgage payments or utility bills. He had little else to spend his money on besides commissary items and the items he wanted to purchase on the black market inside the prison.

In March 2002, a letter was received by District Attorney Rex Gore of Columbus County, North Carolina. The letter was written by a man who had previously been incarcerated at Pasquotank Correctional Institutional. He had been placed in a single cell directly across from inmate L. C. Underwood, approximately twelve feet away. Over time, the two men became friends and began to confide in one another. Approximately two months after they met, L. C. told his friend how he had killed both Viktor Gunnarsson and Catherine Miller. He also admitted to shooting into his ex-girlfriend Kay's house, hoping to hit her teenage son as he slept.

Don Gale located and interviewed the ex-con who wrote the letter to D. A. Gore. The man told Don all of the above which L. C. shared with him. In addition, he said L. C. bragged repeatedly that the police had not found either gun. What Don did not anticipate was that the man had even more information to share, new information that no one else knew about to that point.

He said that L. C. had deposited $25,000 into an account belonging to another inmate, and that money was the down payment on a hit. The inmate, who was about to be released from prison due to being diagnosed with a terminal illness, had agreed to kill someone involved in L. C.'s case as soon as he got released. Then L. C. would deposit another $75,000 in his account, the rest of the payment for killing.

Investigation followed, but there was "insufficient information obtained to indicate the purpose for the payment." In other words, they could not prove that the job was to be a "hit." The inmate with the terminal illness, when questioned, claimed that L. C. had given him the money only as a gift to help with his medical and final expenses. Everyone who believes that, please stand on your head and crow like a rooster. We all knew *what* the money was for; we just did not know exactly *whom* it was for.

Tom Rusher was convinced it was payment for a planned attack against him since he had received the facsimile warning. Don suspected it was really for him, surmising that L. C. had found out about his having developed a working relationship with Lisa Collins, and I presumed it was for me. I was, after all, the lead investigator in the murder case for which he was serving time.

L. C. had even expressed his keen dissatisfaction with his own attorneys, Bruce Kaplan and Chester Whittle, who had been appointed to represent him in the Gunnarsson murder trial and failed to obtain a verdict of "not guilty." Additionally, L. C. had demonstrated sufficient malice and motive to exterminate Kay and/or Jason. As several of the aforementioned individuals sat down together at a conference table to discuss the likely possibilities, I mentally likened us to the twelve disciples at the Last Supper asking Jesus who it was that would betray him. Each of them asked themselves and asked Jesus saying, "Lord, is it I?"

For weeks afterward, I found myself experiencing difficulty relaxing in my own home. I seemed to hear every sound that occurred in my home, and I checked the same locks multiple times each night before going to bed. I looked out the windows at home more than I ever had before. I felt distracted and on edge at work, and frequently ill-tempered from sleep deprivation. Randy and I had even had the propane company check our lines and connections to make sure they had not been tampered with. It took months of no suspicious activity before I began to return to a more relaxed state of normalcy at home. Even then, I remained alert and watchful.

I could not help but worry about my parents who lived near me. They were the salt of the earth. They rarely locked the doors of their home or their vehicles. No matter how I fussed, it was years before they became more security conscious by locking their doors regularly and installing an alarm system. They were honest, hard-working, and trusting folks, and I loved those things about them, but I could not help but worry about them and about all my family – my two brothers, my sister, their spouses, and children too. I kept most of these worries to myself and continued to pray that L. C. Underwood would never include them, or any others to whom I was close, in his evil machinations. I could not bear it.

CHAPTER TWENTY

**"Then shall the dust return to the earth
as it was: and the spirit shall return unto
God who gave it." (Ecclesiastes 12:7)**

As months and even years went by and the threats continued against me, my family, and others, I found myself nearly as disappointed as Kay that there was no further discussion, no plans to prosecute L. C. for the murder of Catherine Miller. I understood the arguments against it. At the same time, however, prisons were becoming even more overcrowded, L. C. was granted parole hearings, and with each one came the possibility of release. Laws could be changed, pardons granted. I knew any number of possibilities could result in the undesired consequence of L. C. walking out of prison a free man.

Additionally, L. C. continued to file appeals, which he continued to lose, that is until 2010 when he filed a typical appeal alleging that the attorneys appointed to him in the trial, Bruce Kaplan and Chester Whittle, had been ineffective counsel for him. A federal judge in Charlotte, known for his atypical decisions, filled L. C. with hope and granted the appeal, which triggered an independent review by the federal Fourth Circuit Court of Appeals in Virginia. When I received the news, I was stunned, but Kay almost suffered a nervous breakdown. Fortunately, the victory was very short-lived.

The Fourth Circuit Court did not address the allegations of ineffective counsel. What the Court did rule on, however, was whether or not the case would have had a different outcome. Their finding was as follows:

"Over the course of approximately three weeks, the state methodically built its case against Underwood by placing before the jury abundant motive and physical evidence supporting its theory that Underwood murdered both Gunnarsson and Miller....With respect to motive, the state presented an abundance of evidence establishing that Underwood was a man who would not take 'no' for an answer when Weden made crystal clear to him that she no longer desired to continue their relationship. In addition to evidence establishing that Underwood sent Weden letters threatening her physical safety during their tumultuous on-again, off-again relationship, the evidence established that Underwood harbored raging jealousy against anyone whom he believed stood in the way of his ability to have a romantic relationship with Weden, including Gunnarsson and Weden's mother, Catherine Miller."

"It's alright Kay; L. C. did not, and is not, going to be released. It was only a small, temporary victory, and it was firmly denied," I reminded her a few days later.

"I know, but I haven't slept at all since I found out what that stupid federal judge in Charlotte did," she said.

"Yeah." I did not tell her that I, too, had lost sleep worrying about it. Kay had no idea just how close L. C. had come to getting released. Don, Terry, Steve, and I were all in contact with one another, and Don and Terry were scrambling, working to get their information together in order to get an arrest warrant for L. C. for murdering Catherine Miller. The main reason D. A. Kenerly had said he wanted to keep the possibility of charges hanging over L. C.'s head was not about to materialize. But we did not dare tell Kay prematurely; no need to get her hopes up about prosecuting L. C. only to be dashed again.

"Kay, listen to this quote from the newspaper on the appellate decision: *The appeals court ruled that the events of the original trial showed that Underwood's conviction was inescapable, regardless of defense strategy*" (*Watauga Democrat*, January 19, 2011).

"His conviction *was* inescapable; I just hope his prison is also."

"Kay…"

"It wasn't just the appeal, Paula," Kay went on. "Kathy, one of my good friends – well I had considered her to be a good friend – Kathy actually called Anne, who has been an absolute rock for me through all of this. Kathy told Anne that she heard about L. C.'s appeal and that she knew all along that there was more to the case than what I had said, as if my mother's and Viktor's murders were somehow my fault."

"Oh, my goodness! What did your friend Anne say?"

"She hung up on her."

"Well, good for her. As for Kathy and others like her, they need to try being informed and not just opinionated; there's a world of difference."

"Exactly."

"Anne sounds like a good friend to you, though."

"Oh, gracious yes! If it weren't for Anne, Vickie, and Diane, I would never have survived all of this. Those three women are true friends; they are my warriors."

"I'm glad you have them in your life, Kay."

"Do you think he will win another appeal?" she asked me.

"I can't imagine it, but I suppose, in all honesty, anything is possible."

Each time L. C. filed a new appeal, I felt tense until a ruling came down upholding the conviction. Then I would breathe a sigh of relief, feeling like I had been holding my breath for days. No other case, no other defendant had ever affected me in such a manner. The emotional roller coaster each appeal set me on was exhausting. No wonder so many law enforcement officers died of heart attacks; the stress alone was murderous.

We would all have appreciated an extra measure of protection, an additional sentence tacked onto L. C.'s current ones, but the more time that passed, the more personnel changed, evidence could deteriorate or could be destroyed, and there was an increased likelihood that key witnesses would be no longer available. Don Gale retired from the State Bureau of Investigation in 2008, and Steve Wilson in 2009. Terry Agner, lead detective in the Miller case, who had been promoted to division chief over the entire Criminal Investigations Division of the Rowan County Sheriff's Office, had his hands full until his retirement in 2011. Although the four of us would gladly have participated in another trial of L. C. Underwood, others would not have been able to do so. Tragically, some of our would-be witnesses which would have been key in a potential murder trial in the Miller case had passed away.

On October 17, 1999, Rowan County Sheriff's Deputy Richard Allen "Rick" Hillard, whom L. C. called and had him run Viktor Gunnarsson's license plate number, was on patrol duty on Highway 601 when a motorcycle flew past him at a high rate of speed. Rick attempted to stop the motorcycle, but the rider refused to stop. Rick chased the motorcycle and had just passed into the neighboring Davie County on a winding road. He drove into an unanticipated curve where his tires lost traction. His cruiser slid sideways, and he struck a tree just off the road. The motorcycle rider did not stop to assist the deputy; instead, he fled the scene. Deputy Richard Allen "Rick" Hillard died on the scene. Several days later, the motorcycle rider, his conscience pricked, turned himself in. Rick, a law enforcement veteran of twenty-one years, left his wife to raise their two children alone. I had found Rick easy to talk to, open and honest, and he still regretted having done that last favor for L. C.

Retired Lincoln County Sheriff Harven Alexander Crouse passed away at the age of 81 at Carolinas Medical Center on August 28, 2002. Sheriff Crouse had hired L. C. Underwood as a jailer, promoted him to a patrol deputy and later a detective. Sheriff Crouse issued L. C. the .38 caliber revolver he would later use to murder Catherine Miller. He served Lincoln County as the elected sheriff and later retired after 28 total years of law enforcement. A new, 58,000 square foot facility, the Harven A. Crouse Law Enforcement and Detention Center in Lincolnton, was named in his honor. Sheriff Crouse was an Army Engineer during World War II.

John Wayne Bendure Jr., the lab analyst who discovered Viktor Gunnarsson's head hairs in the trunk mat of L. C. Underwood's Monte Carlo, suffered a massive heart attack on December 1, 2006. John died that day at the age of 46. He would personally be missed by many, as well as his professional expertise across the state, not only where he analyzed physical evidence in the State Bureau of Investigation crime lab, but also as he regularly testified as an expert witness in a number of violent crime trials. I enjoyed his sharp wit, easy sense of humor, and interesting conversation.

Joseph Patrick "Pat" Baker, an especially good friend of mine, was a Watauga County Sheriff's deputy who initially responded to the scene and assisted investigators where the body of Viktor Gunnarsson was discovered in the snowy woods of Deep Gap, North Carolina. Pat was a constant source of encouragement and support for me during a particularly difficult time in my life, and not only for me but others as well. He served in law enforcement for 29 years, which included working with children as a D.A.R.E. Officer in the local elementary schools. His greatest joys in life were his wife, Mary, and their daughter, Kathleen. Pat passed away at home from a massive heart attack on Sunday, November 29, 2010.

Lieutenant Allen Junior Stout of the Watauga County Sheriff's Office, my direct supervisor who assigned me as the lead investigator in the Viktor Gunnarsson homicide, passed away in his retirement at the age of 59 on July 31, 2015 due to heart-related issues. He died peacefully in his sleep, in just the manner he told me he wanted to die years earlier. In addition to having worked a number of years for the Watauga County Sheriff's Office, he also served as a member of the Watauga Rescue Squad, the Cove Creek Volunteer Fire Department, and was a founding member of the Fire Department in his home community of Beaver Dam. He was devoted to his wife, Hazel, and his two stepchildren, April, and Michael, about whom he spoke often. I grew up with his brother, Paul, attending the same schools together since Kindergarten, and because Paul spoke of him so favorably, always looking up to his big brother, when Allen became my supervisor, I felt that he became somewhat of a big brother to me as well.

Retired Rowan County Sheriff Robert "Bob" Gray Martin of Rowan County passed away on Wednesday, April 13, 2016 at Novant Health Rowan Medical Center in Salisbury at the age of 59. Bob Martin served three terms as the elected Sheriff of Rowan County from 1986 to 1998, and in addition was also a world-renowned bluegrass musician. Detective Terry Agner worked for Sheriff Martin when Viktor Gunnarsson was kidnapped and Catherine Miller murdered in December of 1993. Sheriff Martin was supportive of our investigation from the onset and appropriated the necessary resources we needed from Rowan County, just as Sheriff Lyons had been and done for us in Watauga County.

Gerald W. "Jerry" Wilson, who jointly prosecuted L. C. Underwood in the murder of Viktor Gunnarsson, passed away on September 2, 2017, surrounded by his devoted wife, Karen, other family members, and friends in the Watauga Medical Center. Jerry served the State of North Carolina faithfully under Tom Rusher, the elected District

Attorney, from 1983 until Tom's retirement. We teased them about being our very own *Tom and Jerry* show. Jerry was sworn in as District Attorney on January 1, 2003, where he served until his own retirement in 2014. Jerry prosecuted many of the felony cases I investigated through the years. I thoroughly enjoyed his dry sense of humor and admired the diligence he consistently demonstrated in prosecuting. Jerry died after bravely fighting a long battle of lung and brain cancer. On my last visit with him in the hospital I asked him about his soul, and he assured me that he had settled the matter many years ago when he accepted Jesus into his heart as a young man.

Chester Elmer Whittle, Jr., appointed defense counsel for L. C. Underwood, passed away on June 18, 2018 at the Watauga Medical Center. Chester was previously a Captain in the United States Army, involved in Military Intelligence and Commander of a military police company in Vietnam. He also served as an intelligence officer in the Phoenix Program. Chester and his wife, Jeanne, had a son, two daughters, and two grandchildren at the time of Chester's passing. Chester was also a Sunday School teacher, a fact I did not know until he passed. Chester used to kid with me, calling me "Watauga County's Ace Detective." He was especially kind to me later, in a difficult period of my life, this despite the fact the many courtroom battles in which we were diametrically opposed. During L. C. Underwood's sentencing hearing, when the State was arguing for the death penalty, Chester effectively preached mercy. I can still see him standing before the jury with a large, black Bible open in his hand, and this is what he said:

"The District Attorney said, 'He who showed no mercy now asks for mercy.' And I ask you to look into your own hearts. Are you angry at him? Do you feel hatred? Do you feel like you want to exact revenge, because that isn't the function of the jury. 'Vengeance is mine,' saith the Lord. The function of the jury is not vengeance. The function of the

jury is to fairly and impartially, without fear and without hatred, decide this case...

"Jesus was, the Bible tells us, confronted with a death. The first I want to mention to you, and you may remember, was the adulteress. In those days, the punishment for an adulteress was to stone her to death. Literally what they would do is pick up rocks in a crowd and throw them at her until she was crushed, bleeding, and finally died. In coming upon a scene like this where this is about to go on, they asked Him, 'What should we do?' They were baiting Him again, as usual. And His response was, 'Let you who is without sin cast the first stone.' And those simple words stopped it all.

"A second time, ladies and gentlemen, when Jesus was confronted with a death, it was His own. He had carried the instrument of His death, the cross, to the place of His death. The cross was put into the ground or put down. He was placed on it. He was nailed to it. He was lifted up. And while up for nine hours with a crown of thorns on His head, and as He was bleeding, He was handed drink by way of a sponge which had vinegar on it. He had been betrayed. He had been reviled. He had been spat upon. And as He was, He didn't cause a holocaust. He knew that His mortal life was coming to an end. He had the power to call forth a holocaust upon those that had done these things to Him and stabbed Him. And instead, He said, 'Forgive them (sic) Father, for they know not what they do.' He didn't hate sinners. He hated the sin. And I submit to you, you're being asked to hate the sinner and put him to death. Again, the District Attorney said, 'He who had no mercy now wants mercy.'" Opening the Bible to the Gospel of Matthew, Chester read, *"Blessed are the merciful, for they shall obtain mercy"* from Jesus's Sermon on the Mount. He concluded with the following:

"The State contends there's something wrong with mercy. The State contends you can't be an alcoholic; you are a drunk. The State would have us go back to barbarism. Jesus also said, 'Whatsoever thou doest to the least of my

brethren, thou also doest unto me.' And we can look around in this courtroom and we can find the least of our brethren without any problem at all, can't we? If you have a strong conviction, hold to it steadfastly. And finally, ladies and gentlemen, this is the last thing I'll say to you. When this trial is over, I hope that you will have an opportunity to see whomever it is that you most love and respect, and I would like to think that it would please you to say to that person whom you most love and respect, 'Today, I had the chance to recommend the death of another human being, but the choice I made was for mercy.'

A jury's vote for the death penalty in North Carolina must be unanimous. In the case of The State of North Carolina versus Lamont Claxton Underwood, the jury recommended to presiding Judge Forrest Ferrell, Life Imprisonment for L. C. Underwood instead of the Death Penalty in a vote of eleven for death and one for life. Chester Whittle and his co-counsel Bruce Kaplan needed only the one vote for mercy.

CHAPTER TWENTY-ONE

**"Confess your faults one to another, and pray
one for another, that ye may be healed."
(James 5:16)**

I am still amazed at the speed in which time passes, particularly as I realize that, in all likelihood, I have more years behind me than ahead of me on the earth. Before I knew it, several years had passed before I actually received from Don Gale a copy of the recorded conversation between Lisa Collins and L. C. I did not expect much in the way of sound quality, based on what Don told me at the time. After all, Bill Kenerly had based his decision not to prosecute, even with the additional evidence, on the quality of the recording as well as Lisa's questionable credibility as a witness. Kenerly had also made it clear that he did not wish to explain himself further to me or any of us as to why he had decided not to prosecute in the Catherine Miller case.

Yet as I saw it, there was no legal reason the recording would not be allowed in court because everything had been done by the book. Lisa was party to the entire conversation, and as long as one party is aware that a conversation is being recorded, there is no legal problem. Had we attempted to record their conversation without either of them being aware or having been served notice in advance, then the recording would have been illegal without a lawfully-issued court order.

The federal law that prohibits individuals (or the government in our case) from intercepting and recording private conversations is called the Wiretap Act. However, more than three quarters of states in America and the District of Columbia, including North Carolina, have enacted laws that are commonly referred to as "one-party consent" statutes. Such laws allow individuals to legally record conversations of which they are a party without ever telling the other participating person(s) in the conversation. Because Lisa was a consenting party to recording the conversation, L. C. did not have to be informed.

The first thing I did with the cassette tape I received from Don was get it copied. I took it with me to a local recording studio, Castle Ford Studios of Boone, North Carolina to be copied. The studio was owned and operated by a good friend of mine by the name of Tim Norris. The gospel quartet of which I was a member, Joyful Noise, had recorded our music at Castle Ford Studios several times in recent years, since early 2011 in fact, so I was familiar with Tim's equipment and its capabilities. Additionally, technology in the field of audio had advanced by leaps and bounds in recent years, since the time that Don had submitted the recording to the S.B.I. crime lab.

For chain of custody preservation in the unlikely event that I ever had to testify in court to the integrity of the recording in my possession, I was present the entire time Tim worked on the recording; it never left my sight (or sound).

We began by making clean, unedited copies of the original tape for preservation purposes. Tim and I listened to the entire conversation as the cassette tape was recorded without alteration onto a digital file from which we made multiple copies. I sat in the sound room, stupefied. Even before any of the background noise was removed, I had little problem hearing and understanding most of the words spoken by both Lisa and L. C. Underwood, especially L. C.'s version of the events of December 3, 1993.

What I could not comprehend was why District Attorney Bill Kenerly thought the recording was not clear enough for a jury to understand its contents. Surely my ability to hear clearly what was spoken was not superior to his own, or to anyone else's hearing ability. Even the occasional unintelligible word or phrase was not enough to cause any doubt to a juror that

L. C. confessed to murdering Catherine Miller, never mind the fact that Lisa, credible witness or not, would have been present to testify, albeit with some significant credibility issues, and to corroborate the recording from the wire she wore when she visited L. C. in prison.

At the studio, once the copies were made, Tim set about trying to improve the sound quality, using one of the copies to work with to eliminate the background noise. The busy visiting area of the prison, a large, open room full of hard surfaces, was loud and tended to echo to some degree. I was beyond pleased at how clear the conversation between Lisa and L. C. was, not only after we eliminated some of the background noise, but also *before the original tape was touched.*

Bill Kenerly does deserve credit, in my opinion, for reaching out to the North Carolina Attorney General's Office of Special Prosecutions. At the time, Mr. James "Jim" Coman was serving as the Senior Deputy Attorney General. He had also served as the Director of the State Bureau of Investigation during the time that we were investigating the Gunnarsson and Miller cases. For that reason, he was already familiar with the investigations. We were all, including Bill Kenerly apparently, in hopes that Mr. Coman and/or his staff would agree to prosecute L. C. for murdering Catherine Miller.

After reviewing Lisa Collins' files along with the taped confession, Mr. Coman declined to prosecute for the same reasons Kenerly had declined: Lisa was perceived to be too much of a liability, too unpredictable, and too much of a credibility problem. I read his final decision, dated July 6, 2004, with predictable disappointment:

Dear Bill (Kenerly):

As you know, we have had numerous discussions since I received your letter on October 8, 2003 regarding an individual known to us as Lisa Collins, who had indicated to Ms. Kay Weden, daughter of murder victim Catherine Miller, that she had information regarding the unsolved homicide of Mrs. Miller. Pursuant to that end, you sent me certain tape recordings which I have listened to, and I have had a number of discussions with Special Agent Don Gale of the State Bureau of Investigation. As a result of all of that activity, meetings were attempted to be arranged with Ms. Collins. Those meetings, for whatever reason, did not take place. Recently, I learned that Ms. Collins has apparently run afoul of the law, and presently her whereabouts are unknown. As a result, she is not in a position to meet with us, let alone provide any credible information that might assist us in solving the homicide of Catherine Miller. We have put up with Ms. Collins' excuses for not agreeing to a meeting on numerous occasions, and I have finally come to the conclusion that even if she were to be found and if we were able to obtain any information from her, the impeaching information that we would be required to turn over to the defense would render her probably ineffective, to say the least, as a witness.

As a result, I do not feel that there is any case to be made, especially when it is based on information provided by Lisa Collins. I am happy to return my copies of the recordings. Otherwise, it is my intention to close out the matter. You may certainly share this information with Kay Weden. I am disappointed for her and her family that we cannot go any further with this matter, but it is my view that I do not believe that Ms. Collins would be of any benefit to us, and it would be disastrous to try and reopen the L. C. Underwood matter.

With best personal regards, I remain

James J. Coman, Senior Deputy Attorney General
Law Enforcement/Special Prosecutions Division

Terry told me that Don was hopeful all along that Lisa would again become cooperative, that she would be honest in her statements if he kept believing in her, but Terry remained unconvinced.

"She's told us so many lies we can't believe a word she says. She tells us one thing, and the very next day she just says she made it all up. I'm really tired of dealing with her, wherever she is."

"Do you think she has the guns or knows where they are?"

"Who the h*ll knows? We'll never know! And we will never find those guns."

"So you think Bill Kenerly initially made the right decision not to prosecute?" I asked Terry.

"Honestly, I don't know. But what I do know is this… Bill is one of the most honorable attorneys I have ever worked with, and even when we don't agree and I get mad over a decision he makes, I usually find him to be right in the long run, to have made the right decision. And now (sic) here Jim Coman has basically agreed with Kenerly, and he isn't going to prosecute it for Bill either. But… I do hate it for Kay. She still calls me, asking me the same questions over and again about why we haven't charged him with her mother's murder. I don't know that she will ever have any closure, any peace, unless and until he is. On the other hand, there is no question that Lisa Collins has zero credibility, and I mean zero. That girl has jerked us around with her lies like you wouldn't believe. She's been in prison for fraud, for goodness' sake; that's her thing. She's a con artist. But she would absolutely be destroyed on the witness stand when it came to credibility. We would have all kinds of problems trying to get around that. There would be no getting around it at all, I'm afraid."

"But she clearly gained L. C.'s trust to the extent that he confessed killing Viktor and Catherine to her," I said.

"Oh, she's good. That's my point."

I pondered the extent of Lisa's cooperation, wondering at her thoughts and motivations as she prepared for her visit with L. C. at the Pasquotank prison that Sunday.

Don's voice was easily recognizable on the recording.

...This recorder is being worn with the permission of Lisa Collins. Lisa, is that correct?

"Yes, it is."

Don and Terry drove Lisa to the Pasquotank Correctional Facility in Elizabeth City where L. C. Underwood was currently serving his prison sentence. It was a cool but sunny Sunday not far from the Outer Banks of North Carolina. Don and Terry waited in a separate office, out of view, while Lisa walked into the visitor's area of the prison and sat down at a small table she was shown. L. C. was escorted from another entrance into the room. Lisa stood up and walked slowly to L. C. They were allowed a hug, and then they sat across from each other at the small table. L. C. reached across the table and took both of her hands in his.

"Honey, I can't tell you how good it is to see you," L. C. said. "D*mn! You look good!"

"It's good to see you too, Lamont. And you're looking good as well. Looks like they're feeding you well around here," she said and laughed.

"The food ain't too bad here," he said. "How was your drive?"

"Long," Lisa answered. "And it's really humid today. About took my breath when we, when *I*, stopped for gas."

"Yeah, this is a h*ll-hole for mosquitos. I was out in the yard earlier today, just trying to occupy my time until I could see you."

"Well, I made it, finally. I'm sorry I'm a little late."

"It's okay, Sweetie, you are here now. And I've got some things to tell you…"

L. C. launched into a long story about some lawyer named Richard Mears who was allegedly taking money from inmates with a promise that he could get them released through some loophole in the law. L. C. had allegedly paid him thirty thousand dollars already. But Lisa cut L. C. off.

"Lamont, I don't wanna hear about this."

"Huh? Okay."

"I just know I came to see you. We've got an hour. We've got, we've got less than an hour, and I don't give a sh*t about Richard whoever."

"Okay," he repeated.

"Now I'm not saying it's not important," she began.

"I'll *write* you and tell you. I want to talk about *you*. Are you okay?" he asked.

"I'm ok," Lisa said flatly.

"Are you sure? You're not just saying that?" He rubbed the back of her hands with his thumbs.

"I'm not just saying that. I wasn't expecting him (Lisa's husband) to know that I was here. Cause he's out of town. That's why I picked this weekend to come. So…"

"I know you don't love him. Well, you might love him. But I know you love *me.*"

"Yeah," she answered.

"I'm *gonna* get out of here," L.C said.

"I know you are. I'm gonna *get* you out," Lisa announced.

"I've got to have a break. I can't, I can't live like this no more."

"I'm gonna get you out. I'm gonna go to Gordon's office on my way back." Gordon was an attorney Lisa knew and had supposedly spoken with on L. C.'s behalf.

"I'm gonna get… let me tell you this. I'm gonna get the thirty thousand dollars back and we can pay Gordon that."

"Yeah, we can give him that. Well, he won't even want *that* much for a retainer."

"Well, Lisa, I tell ya, last night I said to myself, and it was all I could do to keep from crying. I… For the first time in my d*mn life, I found somebody that I can truly and absolutely totally love and adore, and I can't get to them. I can't get to *you*. It's killing me! It's killing me inside!"

"It's gonna be okay, Lamont. After all these years, it's gonna be okay. But now we've got some things we need to straighten out." Lisa had prepared L. C. for the discussion they were about to have when she told him she was coming to visit him.

"I know," he said, sighing.

"Okay, Lamont? You know we have to talk about some things."

"Lisa, I do believe that to have a life with you, I'd do *anything*."

"Well, then…"

But L. C. was still talking. "To have you right now, to have a life with you, I'd do anything in this world!"

"Well, you don't have to do anything except clear something up for me," she told him.

"Alright."

"And I want the truth."

"Alright," he said again.

"Lamont, I've carried, I've carried a lot of baggage over this, over all these years, and I have to let it go. Now, in order for you and I move to on, we can't have this thing between us. I've gotta let it go."

"Yeah," he agreed.

Lisa went on. "Now I didn't care about Viktor Gunnarsson, and you know that. He was a murderer himself! You know he did that to Palme. I didn't care about that. But what you did to Mrs. Miller – well, that haunts me."

"I know."

"…and I've got to let it go."

"I know."

Lisa lowered her voice. "Lamont, I need you to tell me what happened from the time, from the time that you went to her house." Lisa's voice trembled at the end of her sentence. She was emotional.

"Don't cry, Lisa."

"I'm not."

"We're gonna get through this," he said.

"I know you don't wanna go back there, but we have to. I've gotta let it go Lamont. It's killing me. I need you to tell me the truth!" she demanded.

L. C. shifted in his chair uneasily. "I didn't mean for it to happen," he said.

"What?" Lisa asked.

"I didn't mean to snap," he said simply.

"I know you didn't mean for it to happen."

"I snapped. I snapped. I, I…"

"You snapped. Snapped over *what*, though? What did she do?"

L. C. squirmed.

"She was your friend, Lamont."

"I just went to her house to talk to her," he finally said.

"You just went there to talk to her about Kay's money?"

"About *my* money," he clarified.

"What money?" she asked.

"The money that little son-of-a-b*tch Jason broke into my house and stole from me, the money that Kay said she would pay me back."

"Was she home?"

"Catherine? Yes, she was home."

"Did she *let* you in?"

L. C. nodded. "Yeah." He leaned back in his chair.

Lisa leaned forward. "It's okay, Lamont. I'll be okay with it. I'll be okay. Just tell me. There's nobody around; nobody can hear us." There were several people visiting with other prisoners in the same large room, but they were all engaged in their own conversations.

"She said she (unintelligible)," he said quietly.

"She said what, Lamont?"

"She said she wasn't gonna pay me the money, and I…"

"She was *not* gonna pay you the money?" L. C. was leaning away from the table again. "Lamont, don't lean away from me; I can't hardly hear you with all these people there. But there's nobody around here listening to *our* conversation!"

L. C. leaned forward again, towards Lisa. "I just reached into my coat," he began.

"But *why*? Why did you have a gun with you in the first place?" Lisa demanded.

"I can't, I can't... It was in my coat."

Lisa's attention was distracted by a guard walking by. "Wait a minute; wait a minute," Lisa warned him.

"I just put my hand in my coat. And it (the gun) was in my coat, I realized. I ain't kidding you. It was in my coat. It was already there!" L. C. explained vehemently.

"You had your coat on?" Lisa asked, for clarification.

"Yeah. She (Catherine) just started..."

"So, she let you in the house?"

"Yeah. She let me in."

"What did you do then?" Lisa asked.

"I confronted her about the money."

"You asked her about Kay's money, the money?"

"The money Jason stole from me, yes."

"And what did she say?"

"She said she wasn't gonna give it to me. And I said, you mean to tell me that..."

But Lisa interrupted him. "Alright. I understand that."

"I just..."

"And then what?" Lisa asked.

"I just snapped. I just snapped and ...shot her."

Lisa frowned. "How do you go from snapping to pulling it... you had to pull it out of your coat pocket."

"I don't know."

"Yes, you do!" Lisa demanded.

"I don't. I don't. If I could..."

"You know what, Lamont? You need to have a better reason than you just walked in there and snapped, that you just went in and killed her. That's ridiculous!" Lisa pointed out.

"No, no, we got to arguing."

"You and Kay?"

"No!"

"Right. No, Kay wasn't there," Lisa acknowledged.

"No, no. Not Kay. Her mother Catherine."

"But why did you go to Catherine to get the money *Kay* was supposed to give you?"

"Because Kay told me to. She told me to go get it from Catherine because *she* didn't have it."

"So, Kay told you to go get the money from her mother that Jason stole from you?"

"Yes! Kay wouldn't pay me. That's what the fight in the restaurant was about. It wasn't because she was with that man!" L. C. was referring to the incident in which he was stalking her and found her at a restaurant with a date. He caused a scene, poured a glass of tea in her lap, and the manager called the police. It was the incident that got L. C. suspended from the Salisbury Police Department.

"I still don't understand why you went to Catherine to get the money back?" Lisa said to him.

L. C. sounded impatient. "Because, Lisa, she told me she didn't have it! Kay didn't have any money. But Kay and Catherine told me that if I wouldn't report Jason to the police and have him arrested for breaking and entering and stealing my money, that Kay would pay me back the money. Lisa, Kay didn't *have* any money!"

"Okay. So, you went over there just with the intention to get your money back," Lisa stated.

"That's it," L. C. said. "But then she said, 'I ain't paying you a thing!' And she started taking up for Jason, and I just got mad. I just got just madder and madder and madder!"

"Lamont, did she grab your arm like you told me when we were in Watauga?"

"Yeah, she did that. She grabbed me; she grabbed my coat like this..." L. C. took hold of his own shirt to demonstrate.

"Well, if she grabbed ahold of your arm, how did you get the gun out of your coat then?"

"Honey, it was, it was an old coat. It had two pockets. She grabbed this pocket (pointing to the outer pocket) and she was telling me to leave, that she wasn't gonna pay me a dime."

"And you did what?"

"You know what I did," he said quietly.

"Lamont, you *tell* me what you did. And then you tell me that you're sorry!"

"You know that," L. C. countered.

"It don't *sound* like you're sorry," Lisa said sharply.

"Don't you think that if I could go back in time that I would?" L. C. asked her.

She didn't answer him. She asked him another question, "Did she know that you were gonna kill her?"

"I..." L. C. looked to his right.

"Don't look away from me, Lamont."

"I, I..."

"Lamont... I came all the way here to talk about this. Now, did Catherine know that you were gonna kill her?" she asked him pointedly.

"I didn't know myself! It happened just like *that*. It was over; it was done. I couldn't do nothing else. I couldn't do nothing else! What was I supposed to do then?"

"But you can't say you regret it."

"Yeah, I can! I say it every day to myself! If I could go back and change it... but I can't change anything!" He was frustrated.

"Would you take it back if you could?" she asked him gently.

"Sure. You know I would take it back if I could."

Lisa considered his response, then continued with her questions. "What did she do when, when you shot her?"

"What do you mean, *what did she do?* She didn't do nothing. I shot her in the *head.*"

"But did she say anything to you beforehand? Did she see it coming? Did she see it when you pulled the gun out of her pocket? Did she see it? Did she know you were gonna shoot her?"

L. C. sighed. "Well, I guess she had to see it. She was facing me, looking right at me."

"What?"

"I said she was facing me, so I guess she had to see it."

"So, she saw. She saw when you took the gun out," Lisa repeated.

"Yeah."

"But you said you went back to her house after you left. Why did you go back to her house?"

"You know why, Lisa."

"Yeah. I know why you went back."

"You know why. So, you don't need to ask."

"But I want you to tell me. You never told me before. But you're gonna tell me *now.*"

"I had to make it look like a robbery," he explained.

"That's why you went back? To make it look like a robbery? Not to check on her and see if she was still alive?"

"She wasn't alive, Lisa." He spoke to her as if she were a child who could not understand a simple concept.

"Do you even care that you killed her?" Lisa challenged.

"Yes, I do! I hate myself for it. But I got to live with it. I've got, I've gotta find a way to live with it. I gotta find a way to."

"To live with it?"

"Yes. Lisa, why do you need to know this?"

"Lamont, I gotta let it go in order for us to move on."

"Lisa, if I could take it back I would. I would take every... I would take *every*thing back! I would take everything I've ever done in my life except meet you. That's the only thing I would never change about my life, the *only* thing. Meeting you was the best thing that ever happened to me, and look where I'm at!

"Lamont, did Catherine die right away?"

"Huh?"

"Did Catherine die right away?"

He nodded.

"Are you sure?"

"Uh-huh."

"But how do you know? You told me you didn't touch her or anything. You told me that when we were in Watauga."

"I didn't touch her."

"Then how do you know she died right then?"

"She didn't have a chance," L. C. said.

"Well, some people have lived after they're shot in the head. Maybe she was alive when you left her."

L. C. didn't say anything.

"Well, how long was it after you left that you went back? Just look at *me*. Don't look around this room, Lamont."

"I don't know, Kay – I mean, Lisa." Lisa ignored his error.

"I need you to tell me, Lamont. How long was it before you left? After you shot her, how long was it before you left and went back?"

"Oh, um, I don't know."

"Like minutes? Hours?"

"Yeah, maybe a half-hour."

"Weren't you *scared*?" Lisa asked.

"Sure, I was. I panicked. I was absolutely panicking," L. C. said calmly.

"Did you see her? Did you go look at her or anything?" she asked.

"I wouldn't... I wouldn't look."

"You didn't go in there – where was it – oh yeah, it was in the kitchen. You didn't go in the kitchen again?"

"Well, I, I came, I came in the same way, through the kitchen door, but I wouldn't look. Anyway, I *knew* she was dead."

His response did not satisfy Lisa. "I don't see how you knew if you didn't check on her. But... I couldn't have done it either. I would've been too scared."

L. C. was staring at Lisa's neck. "...Hey, that's a pretty necklace you're wearing," he said in a childish manner, as if he were speaking to a little girl.

"Gary gave it to me."

"Hmm?"

"Gary. My husband. He gave it to me. And I'm still wearing my wedding ring."

"Huh?" L. C. frowned.

"I said I'm still wearing my wedding ring." Lisa twisted her left hand over in his so that her ring was visible.

"I noticed."

"You're changing the subject."

"...I can't tell you nothing else. I don't know nothing else. I, I've told you everything."

Lisa was getting frustrated. "Okay, first of all you knew that I was coming here to talk to you about this. Didn't you?" She sounded like a schoolteacher scolding a student.

L. C. nodded, and Lisa went on, "So, I have driven six hours here. And if we don't straighten this out, we can't move on. Do you understand that?"

"Honey, I've told you everything!" Even though L. C. was whispering, he was whispering in an angry tone.

"Does it bother you to talk about it?" Lisa asked him.

"Yes, it does."

"Well, you can't say it. You're talking like you can't even say it. There's nobody here... You knew that I came here to talk to you, and you can't really even admit it to yourself what you did. So how will we ever get through this?"

"I have! I have, I have!"

"And you won't even admit it to me?"

"Admit what? Wh-what do you want me to do?"

"I want you to say that you're sorry for killing Catherine."

"I am!"

"Then say it."

"I'm sorry. I am! I don't know what more I can say." L. C. did not care to be pushed, and his patience was running out.

"Okay. I believe you," Lisa said calmly.

But L. C. was angry now. "Do you think I just make it a habit of doing this?" He demanded. His face had turned dark red, and his dark eyes had grown even darker.

"Look," Lisa said, a bit gentler. "I know you didn't *mean* for this to happen. Ok? I know you didn't, because if I thought that, then how could I possibly be here? I love you more than anything in this world. And all these years I have stood by you, and I have protected you, even when you didn't even think that I was. I protected you to no end. And you know it, don't you?"

"Yes, I do. Absolutely," he said, calming down.

"All these years, without fail, through everything," Lisa reminded him.

"Everything… I know," he said.

"But I've gotta let this go."

"Lisa. If it wasn't for you, I would've said the h*ll with it all!"

"Do you know how lucky you are?" Lisa asked him.

L. C. looked down and nodded.

"*Do* you?" Lisa persisted. "First of all, you should never have gone back to Catherine's house. You should never have gone back there! I still can't believe you had the nerve to go back there!"

After a long pause, L. C. answered, "I'm sorry."

"…Do you ever think about her?"

L. C. mumbled in the affirmative.

"Well, you have to let her go too. You know… them showing me those crimes scene photographs?"

"Huh?" he asked, confused.

"Them showing me those crime scene photographs?" Lisa repeated.

"I... didn't know they did that," he replied.

"They sure did. It was...quick. But I was sitting across the counter from them when I was at Rocky Mount, and they showed it to me. I looked at a picture of Catherine in her kitchen, lying there in the floor, and I told them to put it back, that I didn't want to look at that picture anymore. But you know, it was too late then because I'd already seen it."

They just stared at each other for a moment.

"Lisa, I'm not changing the subject," he said (although he was), "but can I ask you a question?"

Lisa looked him impatiently and raised her brow.

"I know you told me you talked to Don Gale, that he had got in touch with you, called you or whatever. You said he came to see you. But then you said he came back another time after you got out (of prison)."

"Yeah. Twice."

"What did he want?" L. C. asked tightly. He hated the man.

"To talk to me," Lisa answered smartly.

"I know *that*. About what?" L. C. asked.

"About this case. What do you *think* he wanted – for us just to *chitchat*?" Lisa said sarcastically.

"Well, no, I..."

"To see if we could be *friends*?"

"I just wondered what he said," L. C. answered defensively.

"What do you *think* he wanted? He wants *you!*" Lisa continued bitingly.

"I know he wants me," L. C. said.

"Well, why are you asking me then?"

"I was just, simply curious... What did you tell him?"

"I didn't tell him anything! What do you mean, *What did I tell him?* Jeez, Lamont!"

L. C. was instantly contrite again. "Don't get mad at me now; we're talking. You said we could talk. I was just asking. I mean, what did Don Gale say to you?" L. C. clearly was not going to let the subject drop without answers.

Lisa sighed. "Don sat down and asked me if I knew anything about this case. He said he found out that you and I were across from each other in the jail in Watauga County. He asked me if I knew anything about the case. I said I might, and I might not."

"When was that again?" L. C. asked.

"It was the first time he came to see me," Lisa said, deliberately vague.

"Was this while you were in jail? I mean, was this while you were in Rocky Mount?" He was referring to a sentence Lisa served in the women's penitentiary in Rocky Mount, North Carolina.

"Yeah."

"Oh, I thought you meant he'd come to your *house*," L. C. admitted, relieved.

"Oh no, he came to the prison," she said (although he had indeed gone to her home).

"Oh! Oh. I was just, I misunderstood what you said. I thought you said he came to your house."

"No!" Lisa denied. "He never came to my house! I'd never invite him over to my house!"

"No! No, Sweetie, that's not what I meant!" L. C. laughed uneasily.

Lisa halfway laughed. "He never came to my house. He came to the prison."

L. C. just stared at Lisa for a few moments, smiling. "You never change. You're as pretty as ever."

"I got my hair all cut off. Look," she tugged at the ends of her short hair.

"It looks good." L. C. leaned forward and pushed her hair back, touching her near her collarbone. Lisa froze for a second, thinking he had felt her microphone wire. "It's cute."

Maybe he hadn't felt it. She leaned back in her chair a bit.

"So, you like it short like this?" she asked, watching his face carefully for any subtle change of expression. She saw no changes. He was still looking at her like a dog looks at a T-bone.

"Yeah. I do," he said. "Lisa, I, I love you just anyway you are. I don't care what you do with your hair. Do you have any idea just how much I do love you? Do you know how, how devoted I am to you? There's nobody else on this earth; there's no other woman that can make me feel the way I feel about you. There's *nobody* else. I wouldn't never leave here for nobody else. And if I ever get my chance..." He stopped when he saw that Lisa was frowning.

Lisa interrupted him, "What do you mean *If?*"

"Well, some days, Honey, I just get so discouraged..."

"I know, but you went from, 'We're gonna do this,' and now you're calling *Ifs.* I can't have *Ifs* here, Lamont. I'm leaving my husband. I'm moving out. I can't have *Ifs.*"

"*When.* I mean *when.* When I leave here and I walk out of that door with you, I'm never leaving you until you, until you bury me. ...I'd never run around on you, Lisa. I'd never want another woman. Never! And I honestly mean that. All these years I've loved only you. Every day I think of you. Even those two years I never heard from you, I often wondered where you were."

"Why didn't you contact me?" Lisa countered.

"Well, Honey, how was I gonna contact you? I didn't know where you were! I figured you went back to Florida. And I figured, h*ll, you didn't want anything to do with me! How was I gonna contact you, Sweetie? I didn't know where to look!"

"But you should have tried," Lisa responded, not showing him any mercy on the topic.

"Deep down, I just didn't think you wanted – I thought that Don Gale, Paula May, and them, that they had got to you."

"You should have known that I would never have done anything to hurt you. You should have known that," Lisa admonished.

"Honey, but under the circumstances, what was I supposed to do?" he asked her helplessly.

"I just couldn't deal with your mother," Lisa said, referring to Barbara, *Bobbie,* the woman in Ohio that L. C. had falsely told various individuals that she was his dying mother.

"I know that she made you mad," L. C. said.

"But I don't wanna talk about her now," Lisa said abruptly.

"I know that, and don't get mad…"

"Hey, I'm not mad at *you.*"

"You just get so mad – boy you get hot…"

"Well, I don't like your mother. She's really a horrible person… I'm sorry, but she is," Lisa said bitterly.

"You know, sometimes I think so myself, Sweetie."

"Yeah. She really is."

"But Burl likes you very much." Burl was Barbara's current husband.

"Look what she did to us," Lisa reminded him.

"Burl thinks the world of you," L. C. said, trying now to shift Lisa's focus.

"I like Burl too. He's sweet."

L. C. motioned to another table in the Visitor's Room. "We sat right over there when we had our last visit, and the only thing I said to my mom was, I said, 'Mom, when Lisa brought the police up to the house and they were looking for guns, she wasn't trying to hurt me. She was trying to help me."

"Yes, I was trying to help you. Yes."

"I told her to think about it. I told her that you could easily have told them that you knew something had been buried there when there really wasn't and caused them to dig up the place, even though she really knew there wasn't nothing there." Lisa was good; she had somehow convinced L. C. that she had not done anything to help Don and Terry, even though she had obviously told them that she had seen one of L. C.'s guns at Barbara's home in Ohio and had accompanied them to execute a search warrant at Barbara's house.

Lisa interrupted him then. "But on the flip side of that, before you say anything else about her, I want to make sure you understand that I have helped you more than I've ever helped anyone in my life. You have to know that by now."

"Yes, I know you have. And I came close to telling my mother right then about us, that we got back together and there ain't sh*t she can do about it."

"I don't care whether you tell her about us or not," Lisa said nonchalantly.

"But I didn't."

"Well, let's face it. What's she gonna do now, break up my marriage? It's a little late for that, so what's she gonna do?" Lisa laughed halfheartedly.

"Nothing. Kiss me," L. C. ordered. Lisa leaned forward and kissed him on the mouth.

"You still kiss good," L. C. said slowly.

"Your lips are soft," she told him.

"Well, they're sure not getting any use in here!" he joked. Lisa laughed. "I would hope not."

L. C. squeezed her hands. "I just, I just often think, every day… Lisa, do you honestly know how much I love you?"

"Of course, I know," she said, frankly.

"*How* do you know?" L. C. asked.

"Because you tell me every single day. If it's in a letter, or a phone call, or a card you sent that I go back and re-read every day, without fail, all these years."

"All these years," L. C. repeated. "All these years."

"I can't believe you still do," she admitted.

"I do. I guess it was meant to be this way."

"But it's not meant to be like *this*," Lisa said, motioning around them in the prison.

"No," he agreed. "I just know I love you. I will never stop that."

He looked at her expectantly. Lisa didn't want to push her luck today.

"I love you, too," she said.

"You know that picture you sent me? I finally saw the dog in it yesterday."

"Oh, did you? The black dog I was holding on my lap when I was wearing that black shirt?"

"Yeah. Was that *your* dog?" L. C. asked.

"Yep. One of them. I've got *three* dogs."

"I didn't even know there was a dog. I thought it was just something on your shirt. I couldn't tell from that picture. It kind of got lost against the black background of your shirt."

"Well, he's black all over."

"Yes, that he is, with big white teeth."

"Yeah, he's a mean dog."

"Can *we* have a dog?" L. C. asked.

"We can have as many dogs as you want."

"I want a little Shelton - Sheltie dog."

"Like the one you had?" she asked.

"Yeah, and that's another thing that bothers me! They accused me of killing my dog. Lisa, that dog was like a baby to me! The D.A. suggested that I even killed my dog!"

"Well, you didn't, did you?" Lisa asked matter-of-factly.

"No, why Lord, no!" L. C. answered, incredulous that she would even ask.

"Well, now, don't look at me like that and back off from me!" Lisa was working hard to keep L. C. close enough to her for the recorder to pick up every word he said. "I mean, let's regroup here. You wouldn't kill a dog, but you would kill a *person*? Come on, Lamont! ...See, that's just what I mean..."

"Lisa," he said quietly. "Listen to me. Look. Look at me."

Lisa met his eyes.

"I can't say nothing else," he said. "I don't know anything else to add."

"It isn't a matter of that."

"I've told you I'm sorry for what happened," he said. "If I could change it, I would."

"Have you asked God to forgive you?" Lisa asked pointedly.

"Sure. Babe, I've even started going to church in here. I go to church and read the Bible."

Lisa looked unconvinced. "Does anybody else know about this?"

"About...?"

Some other visitors were walking by.

"Wait a minute, wait a minute," Lisa said, warning him. "People are walking behind you. Those guards – they just had to sit me right here in front of that control booth, because I was late."

"Yeah."

She went back to her question. "Does anybody else know about Viktor or Catherine?"

He shook his head no.

"You never told *any*body?"

He shook his head again.

"Then why did you tell *me?* "

"Because I love you," he told her.

"Even way back then?"

"I think since the first time I saw you. You was a little snooty, kind of aloof maybe. Wouldn't – didn't wanna talk to me." L. C. teased. Lisa snickered.

"You gave me a Reader's Digest. We talked about the Ebola virus," she recalled.

"You know I'm reading a book on that right now?" L. C. asked her.

She didn't care what he was reading now. "Do you remember that?" Lisa asked.

"Yeah, and I remember being out on that little walk thing, where you walk…"

"Oh yeah – that little concrete thing there in the yard where we had to take our breaks? Yeah."

L. C. reminisced, "…and you was (sic) washing a window and I was laying out in the sun. And you told me you saw me, and I looked so good, it took you forever to wash that window." L. C. never forgot a compliment. He had thought often of her admitting that to him years ago.

"I remember that. Think how long ago that was," Lisa responded.

"I don't forget," he said. That much was certainly true.

"I remember you gave me that Reader's Digest. I remember when you told me that, um…" a guard walked by, eyeing them both. "Isn't it enough that you're around where everybody can see you?"

"Huh?"

"Isn't it enough that you're in a room where everybody can see you? Why do they have to walk around right here where we are sitting?"

"Honey, I don't know. That's just, that's just – He's pretty cool," referring to the guard.

"He was looking at us."

"Yeah, well, I know him. He's, he's a pretty cool dude."

"Whatever," Lisa said.

"So… is Gary hot?" L. C. was referring to Lisa's husband.

"Is he mad? Yeah, he's mad. He thinks… He doesn't know a lot about your case; just like, what he's read. But he asked me if you were guilty."

"He did? What did you tell him?"

"I told him yeah, and that was all that I said. I didn't give him any details that you had told me. I didn't give him anything else. But I knew if I said no, that you weren't guilty, he would've made my life a living h*ll there. So…"

"He kinda hates me, don't he?" L. C. asked smugly.

"Yeah. ...Well, no, I don't think he *hates* you..."

"Is that why I didn't get a Christmas card from him?" L. C. joked.

"How could he hate you? He's never met you. He couldn't hate you. I think he's afraid for me to be involved with you. I think he's worried about my safety."

L. C. shook his head and opened his mouth, but Lisa cut him off.

"I think he's afraid that you'll get out, you know..."

"I would never hurt you. Lisa, if you don't want me, all you'd have to do is tell me. That would be the end of it. I'd leave you alone."

Lisa was not going to let that comment go. "Then why wasn't it the end of it then when Kay broke up with you?"

"Lisa, if I, if I knew what was gonna happen, if I knew that was gonna happen..."

"But you and Catherine were *friends*, weren't you? You told me you did work for her and everything!"

"Yes. I just, I just got *so mad* that night at Catherine. I mean..."

"But you were mad at *Kay*. You weren't mad at Catherine!" Lisa reminded him.

"I know, but I *got* mad at her..." L. C. tried lamely to explain.

"Why didn't you shoot *Kay* then? She's the one you were so mad at!"

L. C. made no comment. He sat for a moment with lips pursed, trying not to lose his temper.

"Don't you wish you had?" Lisa said, and chuckled. "Don't you wish you had shot Kay instead?"

"Yeah, *plenty* of times. But..."

"And that's what Gary's worried about, that you will get mad like that again over something. Gary's worried, and *I'm* a little worried. Not about my safety. I don't think you'd ever hurt *me*, but what you did to Catherine..."

L. C. was not comfortable with the current topic of conversation. He tried to steer it in a different direction. Plus, he wanted to know Lisa's plans. "But you say you're still leaving Gary. Where are you gonna go?"

"I don't know. I don't know yet, but I got, I got…"

"You got *me*."

"Yes, I got you …You're in here, but I still got you."

"Lisa…"

"What are we gonna do about getting you out, Lamont?" Lisa wanted L. C. to tell her what his own plans were. Was he still thinking about trying to escape?

"Well, Gordon, your attorney. Gordon's gonna have to… Gordon still thinks he can win this case, don't he?"

"From everything that he said, yeah."

"Well, then I have to have somebody that's a decent enough lawyer to help me. Lisa, I'm gonna tell you something, and this, this is the God's honest truth. I would rather be dead than live like this and live without you. This is not a way for any human to live. And without you, I don't give a sh*t about nobody. I don't care about me or…"

Lisa interrupted him. "Well, Lamont, don't you feel some responsibility for what you did?"

"Sure, I do!" he responded impatiently.

"I mean, I'm not asking you to torture yourself or anything, but do you know how long it's been since we talked about this? You would not talk to me about it over the phone when I tried to. You told me I had to come down here. So, I came down here. I came down here to talk about this, and you knew that ahead of time. Now, don't act like I'm being an imposition coming down here and asking you questions about it!"

"I'm not! Lisa… Don't say that. You could never be an imposition. Please don't be mad, Sweetie," he said.

"I'm not, I'm not mad at you or anything. It's just that, you know, I don't want you to be upset about all this either. Okay? I feel just as badly for you as I do for Kay's mother.

They are totally different circumstances, but I feel just as badly for you as I do for her. Okay?"

L. C. nodded. "Yes, it hasn't been easy for me."

"I know, but Kay's mother is gone. Catherine can't come back and change things, but you *can*."

"I'm trying," he said.

"I don't want you to be upset either, okay?"

"Okay."

"You didn't mean to kill her, did you? When you went there?" Lisa persisted. "And if you could go back and change it, would you want to?" Lisa was thinking that Kay deserved to hear him say it.

"Yes, Lisa."

"You liked her? You liked Catherine?"

"Yes."

"Was she a nice person?"

L. C. nodded.

"Was she nicer than Kay?"

"Well yeah! Of course!"

"Well, you can't go back," Lisa stated the obvious.

"Lisa."

"Yeah?"

"I've got to let it go myself *some*time."

"Yeah, you do, and I'm not saying that you shouldn't. I'm just saying that we, you know, in order for us to get through this and move on, that we had to talk about it. And after I leave here, we'll let it go. But you, when you get out, why don't you go into therapy?"

L. C. looked up at her like she was crazy.

"I mean, you know how those people are. You don't have to go in there to talk to them and tell them anything. You know, but you can go in there and talk to them... because of *this*, because of being here," motioning around at the prison. "You know? Talk about how being in prison makes you feel and all that." L. C. did not look remotely interested.

Lisa added, "But I think the best therapy is gonna be just talking to *me*, and to go to church…"

Their conversation was interrupted by an inmate walking by. L. C. greeted him cheerfully. "Rocco!"

The man answered, "How ya doing?" and they shared a brief exchange. L. C. introduced Lisa as his fiancé to Rocco.

L. C. told Lisa a little about Rocco but saw that she was not interested in talking about Rocco at all. "I don't think I could ever love anybody else again like I love you, Lisa. Don't even think it."

"Did you love Kay like this?" Lisa asked L.C.

"Oh Lord, no!" L. C. responded quickly.

"Promise?" Lisa asked.

"I promise!" L. C. answered adamantly. "I didn't even love my *wife* like I love you! My wife didn't…"

"Then, Lamont, why were you so jealous of her if you didn't love her?"

"Because I never knew where she was, who she was with, or what she was doing!" As if that explained everything.

Lisa let that sink in.

"Babe, you look so good. I just want to make love to you so badly."

"Here in front of everybody?" L. C. looked around at the families visiting and the children running around.

"Well, not *everybody*."

"I don't think they're gonna let us have that kind of visit," Lisa said, brushing him off.

"Well, if they would, I could take you into the room right there," he said, motioning. L. C. kissed her again.

End of recording.

After all those years, I had finally heard L. C. admit voluntarily that he killed both Viktor and Catherine. God had answered another prayer.

CHAPTER TWENTY-TWO

**"Therefore hell hath enlarged herself, and
opened her mouth without measure:
and their glory, and their multitude, and
their pomp, and he that rejoiceth,
shall descend into it." (Isaiah 5:14)**

By the beginning of 2018, I had finally accumulated enough years of law enforcement service to consider retirement. I had spent the last ten years as Chief of Police in the city of King, North Carolina, a small town in the Piedmont/foothills area of the state. I lived and worked only minutes from L. C. Underwood's hometown of Winston-Salem, where he spent most of his youth in the Methodist Children's Home. I thought of him each time I drove past the old buildings.

The years had passed at warp speed. I remembered as a young detective working for Sheriff Lyons how thirty years seemed like an eternity ahead of me. Now it seemed like the vapor it truly was. Sheriff Lyons was one of the most honorable elected officials Watauga County had ever had, but he too had retired at the end of his fifth term in 2002. In my tenure as Chief of Police, I had relied upon the wisdom and knowledge that Sheriff Lyons had instilled in me more times than I could count.

By October of 2018, I had completed over thirty years of full-time law enforcement service, and I was not only the first female police chief for the City of King, but I was also the longest-running police chief the city had as well.

I had survived a career in law enforcement. My marriage, sadly, had not. Randy and I had divorced amicably and remained friends. He and I both were blessed to reach the age of retirement after thirty years each in law enforcement, having attained a goal far too many in our professions do not because, tragically, they never made it home at the end of a shift.

If ever I intended to pursue another career path, another life dream or goal, or even just to spend time traveling as I so wanted to do but had not previously had the time, I needed to retire while I was young and healthy enough to enjoy it. I did have one specific goal in mind, a goal I felt compelled to accomplish as soon as time permitted... to write the true crime story of Lamont Claxton Underwood and the victims he terrorized.

More than ever before, I believed strongly in the power of prayer, and that I should seek God's wisdom and guidance on every decision, including the decision to retire. I had law enforcement in my blood for so many years, I did not know if I could ever really let it go. I felt that God was leading me, however, to retire at the end of the year. I publicly announced that my last official day of employment would be January 1, 2019.

Once in a while, though, I could not deny the sense of uneasiness I experienced every time I had a passing thought about L. C. Underwood, who was still serving his prison sentence in the North Carolina Department of Corrections. So many, many others, some who were seemingly just as wicked as he, had made threats against me and others from time to time, or otherwise caused me various degrees of concern, but none had really gotten to me as L. C. Underwood had done. Perhaps it was just that I did not know anyone else who hated me so badly or had gone as far as he had tried to go. He had made me fear him, and even years later, the mention of his name stirred it up from somewhere deep inside me.

I wondered if, after retirement, I would still be kept in the loop as closely when L. C. was moved from one location to another, or worse, if he were paroled or escaped. The same old fear of him and the recollection of his many threats against me replayed in my mind. I had seen many law enforcement leaders come and go during my thirty years of experience, and I was aware that the old adage generally applied: out of sight, out of mind. I would be out of sight and out of mind soon. When I retired from law enforcement, would I feel more vulnerable? Would I *be* more vulnerable?

As doubts wafted through my mind, I continued to pray about this matter of L. C. Underwood too, and I seemed to be getting the same answer in response, that I should proceed with retiring from full-time law enforcement service on January 1st. I realize there are skeptics who may doubt that there is a loving Creator God who actively works in the lives of those who will put their trust in Him, but their perspective is a matter of choice, and I respect that. The lack of others' belief does not shake my faith, but the knowledge of what they are missing does sadden me.

Through it all, my Heavenly Father had been – and continued to be – faithful. He has proven to me time and again that His ways are not my ways, and His timing is always best. I determined not to stop trusting His guidance in my life now, and thus I left the business of L. C. Underwood, and my remaining fear of him, to God.

Christmas Day of 2018, twenty-five years after Viktor Gunnarsson and Catherine Miller were murdered, dawned cold and clear. I left my home in the foothills of North Carolina early and drove north on U.S. Highway 421, taking the same basic route that L. C. had taken with Viktor Gunnarsson bound and gagged in the trunk of his car. I drove past the Blue Ridge Parkway where Viktor took his last breath on this earth. I never passed the scene that I did not think of Viktor, and then of Kay and Jason, Catherine, and L. C.

I continued driving north on 421 until I exited left onto U.S. 321 North, driving just a few more miles until I arrived at my parent's home in the rural community of Sugar Grove. I was met with the divine aromas of coffee brewing, bacon, sausage, *and* country ham frying, hot strawberry jam, sausage gravy, *and* sweet chocolate gravy simmering on my mom's stove. I knew there were plenty of other breakfast treats as well, including my mother's homemade biscuits browning in the oven – the best biscuits I had ever eaten anywhere, hands down. My mother always made her famous breakfast for the entire extended family who would all be rolling in at any moment, including my beautiful daughter, Katie, and her loving husband, Jon, my son-in-law of only six months. At that very moment, I was overwhelmed by a feeling of gratitude for one more year with the ones I loved so dearly. Holidays are a time for celebrating with family and friends, and we all had a lot to celebrate, the greatest of which was the birth of our Lord Jesus, who left the realms of Heaven to humble himself and come to earth to save the sinful souls of all mankind.

Several hours later, when everyone had eaten all they could hold and more, all of the Christmas presents were opened, and many of my family members had already gone on their way, I said my goodbyes as well. As I passed Granny Lucy's old house, now occupied by another family, I whispered a quiet "Happy Birthday" to Granny, who was born on Christmas Day 1909, and who moved on to Heaven in June of 2002 at the age of 92.

Reversing my earlier route and traveling south on U.S. 421 towards my house in King, I was barely past the crime scene in Deep Gap when my cell phone chimed.

It was an alert from SAVAN, the North Carolina Statewide Automated Victim Assistance and Notification System, coming directly to me on Christmas Day. I had not received a SAVAN alert in many, many months. My heart began to race as I read the text on the screen. I pulled onto the shoulder of the road and stopped. I read it three times to be certain. Then I dialed the phone number that was provided on the message.

"Am I speaking with Paula May?"

"Yes, ma'am. I'm Paula May."

"Chief of Police in the City of King?"

"Yes, ma'am."

"Chief May, I am calling to notify you that an inmate on your watch list is deceased. Lamont Claxton Underwood passed away while incarcerated at Central Prison in Raleigh."

"What? He's dead?"

"Yes, ma'am. He did pass away."

"Um, are you sure?" I know I sounded unprofessional, but I had to know for sure.

"Yes, ma'am."

"May I ask what happened to him?" I asked.

"It was cancer, ma'am. Kidneys, I understand."

"I wasn't aware – that he had cancer, I mean."

"Yes, ma'am."

"Had he been sick for a long time?"

"I'm… not sure for how long."

"And you're sure the decedent is L. C. Underwood."

"Positive, Chief. Date of birth September 10, 1951."

"That would be him. Thank you for letting me know."

"You're welcome. And Merry Christmas, Chief."

"Merry Christmas to you," I replied.

I could not get in touch with Steve or Terry, but Don picked up on the second ring.

"Well Merry Christmas to us!" Don said cheerily when I told him.

"No kidding," I said.

"I can't believe it," Don kept saying. He sounded extremely relieved, as was I.

There was no denying the sense of relief that accompanied the news of L. C.'s death. But I could not rejoice in his death. I thought about H*ll, his likely habitation, and there was nothing whatsoever that was joyous about that place.

"Does Kay know?" Don asked.

"I don't know. They just alerted me. I called you right away."

"Are you gonna call her?" he asked.

"Unless you want to, I will."

"Well, I am still having Christmas with my family, so why don't you go ahead?"

"Okay then. Can you let Terry know? I couldn't get hold of him or Steve. And I'll tell Sheriff Lyons and Tom Rusher."

"I for one am glad to hear about L.C., and on Christmas at that... Aren't you?"

"Well, I'm relieved that I – that Kay – doesn't have to be afraid of him anymore."

"That's true," Don said.

"Well, you go on and enjoy your time with your family. We'll talk soon," I told him.

"Merry Christmas," Don said and hung up.

I hit "end" on my cell phone and then immediately dialed Kay's number.

"Merry Christmas, Paula!" Kay said when she answered. "It's great to hear from you! How are you?"

"I'm fine, Kay, and how are you? Are you having a good Christmas?"

"I am. It's been a quiet one, but I am spending the day with my cousin, Bo Davis, and his wife, Cindy, who were kind enough to invite me."

"I'm glad you are spending time with them."

"Yes, they live in Irwin, near Campbell University."

"I know where that is. Charlene graduated from Campbell Law School."

"When you talk to Charlene, tell her Merry Christmas from me, and Randy and Katie also," she said.

"I will. But Kay," I began, but she had paused to tell her cousin who was calling her.

"Bo and Cindy, this is Paula May, you know, the lead detective in Viktor's homicide case. She's calling to tell me Merry Christmas," she told them.

"Kay, is Jason with you today?" I asked her but guessed the answer.

"No," she said sadly, "He's not. He and Katie moved to South Carolina. I think they may be spending Christmas with her family, though, in Canton."

"Well, I wasn't calling *just* to tell you Merry Christmas," I said.

"You have news about L. C.?" she asked, instantly alarmed.

"I do," I said slowly. "I take it you haven't gotten any messages about him from anyone today?"

"No," she said, and I could hear the stress in her voice already. "Why? Did he get released for Christmas or something? Oh Paula, is he out of prison? Did he escape?"

"No, Kay, no. Nothing like that. But I do need to tell you something. Are you sitting down?"

"No. Yes. What? What is it?" she said. "Just tell me."

"Alright. Kay… L. C. is dead."

"What? He *died?* "

"Yes. I just received notification, and I confirmed it before I called you."

"Oh Paula, are you sure? Are you certain?" Kay could barely get the words out.

"Yes. I received the notification, and I called Central Prison to verify and get what details I could."

I heard a wail – not wailing, exactly, but some kind of emotional human sound. Then I heard it again. Was that Kay crying? Was she mourning?

"Kay, are you okay?" I asked after giving her a moment.

I heard what sounded like someone blowing their nose.

"Yes, I, I just… I'm crying because I'm so relieved. So happy! But what happened? Did someone kill him in prison?" Kay was finally able to ask.

"He was sick. Kidney cancer. He was in the hospital when he died."

"Did you know?"

"That he was sick? That he had cancer? No, I didn't know." I could hear that sound again. "Kay...Kay, are you alright? Are you there?"

After a few seconds, Kay said, "Paula, I am just so relieved! I feel like someone has just taken the weight of the world off my shoulders!"

"It's a lot to take in. I'm kind of in shock myself," I admitted.

"I am too! I'm just... overwhelmed!"

"Right."

We talked for a bit, and then something occurred to me.

"You know what's ironic?" I asked her.

"What?"

"All the people he told those lies to about his so-called mother having cancer, about to die of cancer, having died of cancer... Now he died from it."

"That's so true!" she said.

"And maybe it isn't as much irony as it is reaping what you sow, mocking God about such things."

"That is exactly what he did!" Kay exclaimed. "And he had *no right* to say such lies about that woman to try and manipulate what few friends he had!"

"No, Kay, he did not."

"Paula, you just gave me the best Christmas present anyone could have given me," Kay said through her tears. "Now, just maybe, I can get my life back. Now maybe I won't feel as if I have to keep looking over my shoulder. Paula, it has been just awful being so afraid. And Jason – Jason is practically estranged from me."

"Oh Kay, I'm so sorry. I didn't know. I thought Jason would be okay by now."

"He, he still blames me for bringing L. C. into our lives. But now, now that L. C. is gone for good, just maybe now things will be different."

"I hope so, Kay. I will pray for that."

"Yes," Kay said, "Please. I have missed my son so much! I am grateful that he married a wonderful young woman who loves and cares for him. But I miss just being a mother to him, you know?"

"I know, Kay."

"They want so much to have children. Jason always wanted a family of his own. They haven't been able to get pregnant. Did I tell you that?"

"Yes, you did."

"I only know that much because of what Jason's wife told me in one of our infrequent conversations, which seem to occur when Jason is off at work or somewhere else." Kay's voice was breaking as it nearly always did when she spoke of her son Jason and her tenuous relationship with him.

"I really hate that you and Jason have not been close," I told her.

"So do I. Jason has basically kept me at a distance for all these years." She was crying freely now.

"I know, Kay. I know, and I'm sorry."

"All I've ever wanted was for my son to be happy... and safe."

"I know."

"But now... Now that L. C. is gone, maybe, just maybe..."

"Maybe so, Kay. Maybe so."

I ended the call so Kay could talk with her cousins and also so that she could have some time to absorb the fact that L. C. was truly gone. I had more phone calls to make. But I had to take a moment and acknowledge with thanksgiving that there was One who was mighty and far, far greater than I, who was ultimately in control of everything, the one true God who was taking care of Kay, her son Jason, and of us all. I was overwhelmed with relief, with gratitude for having been kept safe from L. C. Underwood since the day he determined to kill me. I experienced an array of emotions that would stay with me for days to come.

I called Charlene. She picked up on the second ring.

"Hello?"

"It's me," I said, not knowing whether to laugh or cry. She must have heard the emotion in my voice right away.

"What's the matter?" she asked, by way of a greeting. She knew me well. I could not keep it together any longer, and I could not speak audibly.

"Paula, what's wrong? Are you laughing or crying?" she asked.

"Yes! I mean, I don't know! I don't know what to do, and you're not going to believe it. I mean it's Christmas Day, after all!" I exclaimed.

"What? What is it? Please just tell me!" she pleaded.

After another moment or two of trying to compose myself, I regained the ability to speak plainly. I had held it together to make the phone calls required, but now that I had Charlene on the line, I could release my emotions to my good friend. She had been my rock throughout several difficult times of my life. Her logical approach to life and settled faith had a steadying effect on me.

When I was finally able to make her understand through my blubbering that L. C. Underwood was no longer among the living, she summed up her own feelings with five simple words of cheer.

"Merry Christmas to us all!" Charlene's relief was undeniable. She had observed the effects of L. C.'s threats on me for years, as well as the sheer trauma that he had exacted on Kay. My own emotions were not so clear cut. L. C. was gone from our lives, but he was not gone entirely. His spirit resided somewhere. I could practically smell the brimstone.

I thought about the place called H*ll, and all the time and opportunities L. C. had been given to repent and turn to Jesus. I had no indication that he ever truly had. It did not seem right to rejoice in anyone dying, lost without God and going to H*ll. I could not deny that I felt overcome with relief at the news not only for myself but also for Kay, Jason, and the others he had terrorized for years, but I could not delight in it; neither would I pretend to do so.

I received calls, texts, and messages from Kim Scott and other good friends who remembered the case well, as word spread about L. C.'s death in prison.

On December 28, 2018, I posted the following on my personal Facebook page:

"He was given a life sentence, but ultimately (sic) he got the Death Penalty. In fact, I was condemned to die, and so were you. We all have a divine appointment with death. Hebrews 9:27. "But Jesus said in John 10:10, The thief cometh not, but for to steal, and to kill, and to destroy; I am come that they might have life, and that they might have it more abundantly." In 1997 L. C. Underwood was convicted in Watauga County of First Degree Kidnapping and First Degree Murder, and sentenced to Life Plus 40 Years, but even if he had served both entire sentences, it would be still but a vapor, only a moment's duration when compared to all eternity incarcerated in Hell. But there is one escape, one hope for mankind, one remedy for sin, one intercessor, one mediator between God and sinful man. The answer is God's own Son, Jesus Christ, whose blood can wash away sin, turn the blackest heart white as snow, and make the vilest sinner clean. Acts 4:7 "Neither is there salvation in any other: for there is no other name under heaven given among men, whereby we must be saved."

On Christmas Day I was notified that L. C. Underwood had died in prison due to a serious illness. While there was a sense of relief concerning his threats of deadly force, endless appeals, and years of wondering if he will get out of prison, I keep thinking about him being lost and going to Hell. We can only hope that in the last few days of serious illness he believed in Jesus Christ and asked him to save him. Friend, have YOU?? Your appointment is getting closer all the time."

Others did rejoice at the news of L. C.'s death. But I continued to dwell on the fact of how long eternity really is, and how torturous h*ll must be, in utter darkness without the presence of God or love (for God *is* love), and how hot the lake of fire would be…forever.

I wondered about L. C.'s final days, if he ever, by some miracle, sought God's forgiveness for taking the lives of Viktor Gunnarsson and Catherine Miller and for terrorizing Kay and others. No one I spoke with could provide any indication that he had, other than the one time Lisa Collins had asked him the question the day she wore the recording device into the prison at Pasquotank. Even then, however, his attempts to manipulate and his efforts to say anything to appease Lisa were evident to me as I listened to the intonations, modulations, and inflections of his voice, that voice that spewed out pure evil, that voice I knew so well.

I contacted Central Prison again. I asked both hospital and prison personnel about L. C.'s personal property, writings, and so forth. I learned that those things were disposed of immediately. I supposed the overcrowding situation called for a quick turnover of available cells. I did not learn much more about L. C.'s illness and death, except that he would be cremated, and his remains buried at the Central Prison Cemetery. He had never gotten out of prison, and now he never would.

Having obtained little information from Central Prison, I considered the people who may still have been in contact with L. C. up until his death. Bobbie, the woman in Ohio he referred to as his mother. would not want to hear from me, much less share information with me about

L. C.'s final days. L. C.'s law enforcement friends had long since cut any remaining ties with him.

Then I considered Lisa Collins.

The more I thought about her, the more I wanted to reach out to Lisa directly. Don Gale provided me with Lisa's email, as he had heard from her from time to time over the years. She had not been in trouble for some time now, and he told me that based on her communications to him, she had gotten her life on a positive track. I was happy to hear that. A life of crime is no life at all.

Crime truly did not pay in the long run. Instead, it robbed those wrapped up in a criminal lifestyle of a sense of normalcy, peace, and contentment. Living your life while constantly looking over your shoulder was no way to face the future, no matter how lucrative a criminal enterprise may seem at first. I had seen far too many lives, too many families destroyed by it, whether it was white collar crime, drugs, or basically any criminal lifestyle. I love happy endings, and true tales of salvation and redemption. Jesus came for the sinner, not the righteous; everything and everyone he touched, he changed for the best. Lisa had mentioned the forgiveness of God in her recorded conversation with L. C. I hoped she had personally experienced it as well.

Powering up my laptop, I debated with myself as to whether or not Lisa might resent my reaching out to her at this point, but ultimately, I chose to do so. To my surprise, she responded promptly and straightforwardly. We began communicating, and I learned that she had indeed gotten her life on track. I found her to be an intelligent and articulate woman who had fallen victim to the trap of addiction several years earlier. She candidly told me that she had "unraveled" in her home state of West Virginia, that she spent the next couple years entrenched in an on and off, but mostly on, addiction to pharmaceuticals that plagued her since she was about thirty years old. She told me that her behaviors early in her life were not born out of drugs, but that it was drugs in later years that would merely exacerbate the behavior. The good news, however, is that Lisa informed me she is finally free from the deadly lure of narcotics. She told me bluntly in her correspondence the following, and it is with her consent that I share it here.

"I have fought and carved and scraped together a life here. Something I never thought I would be able to do is stay in one place, make any connections, do anything positive... not with all the destruction, the defects...the choices. People and animals here in my life actually depend on me, and I come through. I often have to ask myself, what would a healthy person choose, what would they do, and I think of someone I know that's a good person, that lives by example here and I do that. Most of the time now though, I don't have to ask anyone to help me, in whatever the need may be. I ask God to guide me, and He does."

I commend Lisa on her success thus far. As I anticipated, Lisa did remain in contact with L. C. throughout his prison sentence, until his death, but she acknowledged that they never had what she felt was a healthy relationship. I asked her if their relationship was ever healthy, ever positive.

She said, "At first, Lamont was protective over me. He even protected me when I first met him in the Watauga Jail. When another man would try to talk to me, Lamont would simply threaten to kill him if he didn't shut up. He said that to any man that would try to talk to me or make crude remarks. I was grateful that most people were afraid of him."

"Even though he was behind bars?" I asked.

"That would never stop him," she said.

She shared with me in writing more of her initial observations of L. C.:

"I spent hours without end talking to Lamont, listening to him read to me, or whatever. I should have been on my mattress seeking God and Mother Mary. I was raised in Catholic schools. Instead, I was talking to Lamont, being seduced into his psyche, I guess. I allowed myself to be. He was kind to me, though at the time he was off a bit, controlling, but he seemed to do this out of a sense of caring for me so I pushed my warnings aside and decided I

would get to know him and his story. I listened to the same rehearsed, pat answers and then how everyone was out to get him and set him up. He was the victim, and he played it really well.

"At first, I remember thinking ok, well maybe police frame people. It happens. But then I read the case files and all the discovery that Chester and Bruce brought him, I began to realize what he was telling me was bullsh*t, and I told him so. I read over pages and pages as Lamont picked them apart and picked out each person that he was particularly going to make suffer: Don, Terry, you, Kay and Jason, Tom Rusher, a man named Steve, and one of his foster brothers. Lamont's hatred was such for you and Don specifically that I began to absorb it too. I can't explain it, I changed. I was angry all the time. I felt hatred and darkness in my heart even towards my family. Lamont was the only person to share that with because he was so filled with it himself. I felt the change, but at the time I did not recognize that I let the evil in...

"I began telling him that he was telling too many conflicting things to me and if he wasn't going to tell me the truth, I didn't want to talk to him anymore. I shut my window and for two days started to feel better, lighter, hope that something better was coming into my life. But then the next day he called me to the window and said he thought he could trust me and that he had feelings for me. Two months in, he began to tell me what he had done. I absorbed it all, night after night, week after week. I began to care for him too. There was something wrong with me, some defect that others couldn't see in me yet, but I felt it. Darkness, apathy. He told me about murdering Viktor and how he did it, but eventually he told me about Mrs. Miller, and other instances, like Beth that you mentioned. He said she had a little girl, that Beth smoked, that she was a wh*re, that she had hurt him, so he would hurt her by turning on the gas and leaving because the first thing she would do is light a cigarette and her apartment would blow up. I asked about the little girl

of Beth's. He said she will be just like her mother. He knew you had/have a daughter too. He wanted to blow up your house with all of you inside. He fantasized about what he wanted to do to all of you, except it was not really fantasy; he intended to do it."

"You heard him say all the terrible things he had done and still wanted to do. Yet you still cared for him?" I asked.

"...Even during those times and the things Lamont and I did to hurt one another, I loved him, insomuch as to the extent that I was capable." She knew even better than I that no good could come of that type of "love."

Finally, I asked Lisa if L. C. ever found out about the recording she made when Don and Terry drove her to visit him in prison, and if she thought he ever experienced any sincere remorse for killing Viktor Gunnarsson and Catherine Miller.

"...Yes, he knew about the tape recording. (He found out) years later, during an appeal, his last one in 2010, I believe. I don't know who disclosed it or how, not for certain anyway. He hated me for it and would spend a decade telling me so and telling me I would never get to Heaven now. (He said) I was a snake, over and over again for doing that to him. He really did some horrible, frightening things to me after that... Those things didn't really stop until he died. Even when Lamont was not physically capable of reaching me, he was more dangerous in his mind, and the time he would spend writing horrible letters, plotting, and planning, and paying people that were being released to contact me or find me or try to scare me! Sometimes it did. No one would help me, though, when I did reach out for help, not the Department of Safety, not the prison he was in. No one. I had to take care of these instances myself in ways I cannot discuss or ever tell."

In 2002, when news of L. C.'s tape recorded confession somehow reached him, Lisa and her husband Gary were living in Mount Holly. In late August, Lisa and Gary discovered that Charlie Frick, L. C.'s private investigator friend was outside their home in the middle of the night, watching them and taking photographs. Lisa's attorney mailed a letter of warning to Charlie Frick on September 5, 2002. To my knowledge, Mr. Frick did not respond. Charlie Frick was the same man who had frightened Kay when she lived in Cullowhee.

I certainly understood Lisa's fears, the same basic fears that Kay, myself, and others had also experienced. L. C. had indeed left a wake of terror wherever he went. His being in prison did little to relieve any of the terror he incited. Some would say it only intensified it. What I did not understand was Lisa returning to L. C. as she did many times over the years. In any event, she did not care to have some private investigator stalking her. Neither did Kay. Neither did I.

I could not help but wonder if Charlie Frick was at one time outside my rural home in Watauga County where we used to live, and if he was the reason L. C. knew I had a propane gas-powered furnace in my house and a propane gas-powered stove in my kitchen. I left messages for Mr. Frick to return my calls, but never received a response. Perhaps he did nothing more than any licensed, self-employed private investigator does, and that was to gather information for his paying client. I just had a real problem with a paying client who was also a convicted murderer, a man possessed by first degree rage.

Lisa readily admitted to me that she was unsuccessful at permanently removing L. C. from her life, despite her moving from town to town, and despite her marriage to another man which ultimately ended in divorce.

"Lamont would always...find a way to call, find a way to pull me back to him and I allowed it...every, single, time. I also initiated the contact as well. I knew he was ill, but I did not believe he was really terminal, dying. That's what happens when you are not genuine though, when you cry wolf, when trust is an illusion. I used to do that to others, but not anymore, not in a very long time."

Lisa confided that she never stopped caring for L. C., or *Lamont*, as she referred to him. I thought about the many domestic violence victims I had encountered throughout my career, victims of both physical and mental abuse, many of whom endured it for years. I strove to impart to each that there was never anything wrong with caring for a person or even loving a person unconditionally. But that care, that love, did not require them to be a punching bag for the rest of their lives. We can care, we can love, we can pray for another person at a distance, a safe distance, without having to remain trapped in the dysfunctional, and often deadly, tangle of their lives.

Lisa was fortunate, as I saw it, in that she never had the opportunity to attempt to create a life with L. C. outside his prison home, as they had discussed. No woman had ever achieved success at that; in fact, each woman I knew who had attempted it, had barely escaped with her life.

I marveled at the depth of emotion, even dysfunctionally, that one person can have for another.

Lisa stated, *"Protecting him (Lamont) never left me, even after he died. I didn't know he had died though, only that he was ill, not until I received a letter in the mail in January from him right after the fact. I cannot share it, but I will say this to you...There was no remorse, no contrition, no acceptance, no accountability....no reference to Heaven or God...It's heartbreaking really to me for his soul. I think about it often and wished I could have changed him for the better. Maybe in his last breaths he asked Jesus to save him. I don't know. I realize we are all passing through and so I find great comfort in the verse... My house has many mansions, if it were not so I would have told you, I go there to prepare a place for you...I don't know who I'll see there, but the only face I need to see is the face of God and know that I made it home...."* She was speaking of the scripture in chapter 14 of the Gospel of John. Verse 6 of that chapter reminds us of who Jesus really is: "Jesus saith unto him, I am the way, the truth, and the life: no man cometh unto the Father, but by me." Jesus is the only way to Heaven for anyone, for everyone, for whosoever will.

In Lisa's final letter to me, she expressed her overall sense of L. C. as an individual.

"Lamont was a coward; he was cruel and unkind. He was other things too; we are all other things. You do not have to contact me again. I trust that you are writing a wonderful story that will help Kay and her son and all of you, hopefully. I think that anyone that reads it and finds commonality or healing or warnings, they will feel less alone, I hope. Whatever you write about me, Paula... it could never be uglier than what really is, so it's okay. God bless us all and take care."

We had shared other exchanges prior to that one, and I did my best to convey to Lisa that I did not wish to do or say anything to cause her harm or embarrassment, that I only wished her the best, and that I appreciated her candor as well as her strength and perseverance. I also shared with her the simple truth that we are all sinners born into a sin-cursed world, that the righteousness of us all is as filthy rags before the holy and righteous God of Heaven. It is the very reason He sent His Son Jesus to die on the cross of Calvary, to pay the sin debt for each and every one of us. She acknowledged the truth of the gospel I shared. The difference between Lisa and others I knew with similar human struggles was that Lisa was brave enough to describe herself just as she saw herself in the harshest and most revealing light. Kudos to her for having no disillusions about who she was or the past from which she came, and for her courage in tackling her addiction and habits head-on.

After I received Lisa's latest correspondence, I felt that I should not trouble her any further or bring back additional hurtful or shameful memories that might discourage her from the progress she was apparently making. Therefore, I did not contact her again, though I pray for her continued success, freedom from the chains of addiction, and above all else, peace.

CHAPTER TWENTY-THREE

**"Therefore my heart is glad, and my glory
rejoiceth: my flesh also shall rest in hope."
(Psalm 16:9)**

"Hello. Paula?"

"Yes, this is Paula."

"My name is Tracy Ullman. I am a television producer at Red Marble Media in New York, New York." It was Valentine's Day of 2019.

"Okay. Well, Happy Valentine's Day to you."

"Why, thank you! And Happy Valentine's to you as well!"

I listened then as she explained the reason for her call.

"The series I produce is Dead of Winter for Investigation Discovery. Have you heard of it?"

"I actually just saw an ad for it on IDTV."

"Right. Have you watched any episodes?"

"I have not."

"Okay. Well, the show is about true crimes, murders, that take place in the winter…"

As she talked, I typed "Dead of Winter IDTV" into a search engine on my laptop. I read the following description of the television series:

"In winter, the world is at its most merciless. As snow falls and darkness descends, people retreat into their homes and brace against the cold. This is a time of isolation and of fear. DEAD OF WINTER tells haunting true tales of murder set in the starkest conditions. From a body frozen in the snow,

to a woman who vanishes in icy wilderness, each mystery unfolds in winter's eerie silence…"

I pictured Viktor Gunnarsson's bare feet protruding out of the snow. I knew why she was calling before she even asked.

"We are aware that the police officer you charged with the murder and kidnapping of Viktor Gunnarsson recently died in prison."

"He did."

"Lamont Claxton Underwood?"

"Yes, ma'am."

"The case was also featured on *Forensic Files*?"

"Yes, it was. Season 10, Episode 39. Before that, it was also featured on a TV series on the Discovery Channel called *The New Detectives*."

"Do you know which season it was aired on *The New Detectives*?"

"Yes. Season 6, Episode 5."

"It was – and is still – an intriguing case, especially with the victim, Viktor Gunnarsson, having been charged with the assassination of the Swedish Prime Minister."

"Yes, ma'am."

"In fact, the Palme assassination has not been solved to this day, isn't that correct?"

"That is my understanding. It remains unsolved, much to the chagrin of the Swedish people."

"We would like to feature the case on *Dead of Winter*, but from a different angle than what the other two shows addressed. Not so much the forensic evidence, interesting though those elements are."

"What kind of angle?"

"More of a personal one," she said.

Tracy Ullman explained that they were interested in how the case had affected three people in particular. "We work first and foremost with the victim's family. For this program, I would like to have yourself, Kay Weden, and her son, Jason Weden, participate and tell the story of just what happened in Salisbury in 1993, and how the entire case has affected each of you *emotionally*."

I was not sure how I felt about that. After all, I had lived for many years with the fear of L. C. Underwood's threats hanging like a dark cloud over my head, and I had only barely begun to process the fact that he was deceased. But it was Kay whom I thought most vulnerable. I had not talked directly with Jason in years and, based only on the things Kay had shared with me about her strained relationship with Jason, I had my doubts as to whether he would even entertain the idea.

"I'm not asking for an answer today. I'd like for you to watch some of the episodes before you decide," Tracy requested.

"I can do that," I told her.

"I'm happy to answer any questions or concerns you may have about it."

"Fair enough," I said, "but I do think the person to ask first is Kay Weden. I would not feel comfortable doing it without her support. Frankly, she's been through enough. If she feels like it would be a positive thing, I will consider it. But if she doesn't, if it will cause her pain to go through it anymore, then I won't. It was my investigation, but it's her life. Hers and Jason's."

"I understand, and I am sure Kay will appreciate your consideration of her feelings."

"And Jason's," I reminded her.

"Absolutely," she said.

I watched several episodes of the show and was pleasantly surprised. The shows were well done. Kay called me before I had a chance to call her.

"What do you think about the TV show, Paula?"

"Totally up to you and Jason."

"I think I'm ready. I feel like I'm ready. Jason said, 'Let's do it, Mom.'"

"Wow. Well… good enough then! I will let Tracy know."

"They want to interview Don Gale also."

"Is Don on board too?" I asked.

"He is. And Paula?"

"Yes?"

"When I was finally able to process the fact that L. C. was actually gone, I realized something. I realized that I need to stop merely existing. I want to *live*."

"Well said, Kay."

"I'm nervous about this TV program, but I want to do it. I see it as an opportunity to do something positive, even though it's a little scary. I think I would regret it if I didn't."

"I support you totally on it then. Fear is only temporary; regrets are forever."

The English teacher in Kay came out then. "I believe it was Ralph Waldo Emerson who put it something like this... What you are afraid to do is a clear indication of the very next thing you need to do." She suddenly sounded like Sheriff Lyons quoting the Bible or Babe Ruth. Her newly emerging, positive approach to life was delightful.

"Then let's do this very next thing," I replied.

The episode was entitled "Cold Blue," and it would air for the first time on television on January 9, 2020, episode 2 of season 2 of *Dead of Winter*. It would be the third time the case had been featured and aired globally on three different television series over a period of more than twenty years. I still never starred in any laxative commercials.

The filming was scheduled to take place at a house in Charlotte, rented by the production company for one week, just for the filming. An entire day was set aside just for the videotaping of Tracy's interview with me. The production crew members were professional, friendly, and hospitable. They put me at ease right away. Another day was dedicated to Don's interview, and another to Kay and Jason.

It was a busy week for me as I had a tour to direct, having had the good fortune to be hired by Burke Christian Tours of Maiden, North Carolina, as a part-time tour director. They offer tours all over the world, and as I was looking forward to traveling in my retirement years and also wanted to keep working with the public, I decided to apply. The day after my interview with Tracy Ullman was filmed, I headed to Washington D.C. with a motorcoach load of energetic, excited middle school students and their chaperones to lead them on a tour of our nation's capital. I did not, therefore, have the opportunity to observe the videotaping of Don, Kay, or Jason.

"Are you enjoying your retirement gig with Christian Tours?" Kay asked me, on an unseasonably warm April afternoon, about a week after the filming was complete.

"Loving it," I told her.

"I'm glad. After years of teaching kids of all ages for about 33 years, I am trying to relax and enjoy whatever years I have left."

"I hear you, and you deserve that."

"Were the cherry trees in bloom on the National Mall?" she asked.

"Yes!" I answered enthusiastically, "and all around the Tidal Basin. Ten to twelve main varieties," I said, in my official, and newly acquired, tour director voice.

"Why cherry trees, I wonder? Who planted them?" she asked.

"I am so glad you asked. They were a gift to the District of Columbia from Japan in 1912. The most common varieties you will see are the Yoshino and the Kwanzan. The Kwanzan cherry trees are the main ones we saw blooming last week. They are my favorites because they have these big pink double blooms that resemble carnations, and they generally bloom a couple weeks later than the Yoshinos."

"Do you know why they gifted them to us?" she asked, always a teacher.

"As a matter of fact, I do. It is a common question asked on our spring D.C. tours. It was a gift symbolizing the spring or renewal/rebirth of a growing friendship between the

United States and Japan. The mayor of Tokyo City, Yukio Ozaki, sent us 3,020 cherry trees via the freighter ship *Awa Maru*, and then into the city by insulated railroad cars. I think it was on March 27, 1912 that First Lady Helen Herron Taft and Mrs. Iwa Chinda, wife of the Japanese Ambassador, planted the first two cherry trees on the banks of the Tidal Basin, near what is now the location of the Martin Luther King, Jr. Memorial."

"It sounds like you really are enjoying your new job," Kay said and laughed.

"...But actually, the real credit goes to a writer from Iowa," I continued.

"Oh really?"

"Her name was Eliza Ruhamah Scidmore, and as a result of her many travels, she mounted a crusade to set cherry trees in Potomac Park for twenty years before that. But it was not until First Lady Taft took an interest in the project that it actually came to fruition. The gorgeous cherry blossoms became quite popular over the years, and in 1934, First Lady Eleanor Roosevelt led the opening ceremony of the first Cherry Blossom Festival in the city."

"Fascinating!" she said, sounding genuine. "I saw parts of the Cherry Blossom Festival on TV a couple of weeks ago."

"Oh yeah? And speaking of TV, I really enjoyed working with Tracy and her crew! So, how was your experience with the interviewing and the filming?"

"It went very well," she said. "In fact, Paula, it was the best thing we could have done," Kay said.

"Really? In what way?" I asked.

"Well, it gave me a chance, finally, to tell my story from my own perspective. I needed to do that, and I needed to deliver the message that no one is above being victimized. What happened to me can happen to anyone if they are not paying attention, if they ignore the red flags, the warning signs in a person."

"Well said, and I'm sure you did a great job, Kay. I am proud of you for the strength you displayed to do that." I thought of the many times that Kay called me, almost paralyzed with fear. I also thought of how sad she had become as several of her friends and basically her entire support system had slipped away from her, one by one. I thought of all she had lost.

Suddenly, however, I realized that there was something new, something restorative in her voice. She had my attention.

"Thank you. But that's not the best part!" Kay said excitedly. She sounded more optimistic than I had ever heard her, almost ...*joyous?*

"What's the best part?" I asked Kay excitedly. Her mood was contagious, and I did not even know why.

"Jason!" she said gleefully, as if the exclamation of his name was explanation enough.

"Okay, but what *about* Jason?" I asked, but all I heard in response was laughing... or sobbing? Kay continued, "We talked; we talked and talked..." Kay's voice broke.

"Kay? Kay, are you okay?" I asked. "I thought you were happy. *Are* you happy? What is it, Kay?"

"It's the very best part!" she repeated. She continued to sob with overwhelming emotion of... joy? Sadness? Relief? All of the above? I waited.

"Oh Paula!" she cried, finally able to speak coherently. "Paula, I think... I think I finally have my son back!"

I listened as she cried. A tear or two escaped my own eye. Her relief was palpable. In between bouts of weeping, Kay told me that the television show had provided Jason and her the opportunity to come together at a neutral location, filming the show and hearing what each other had to say in response to the questions asked, and to engage in honest, candid conversations about the mutual tragedies they had experienced.

"Jason is older now," she told me. "He is doing his best to perceive the things that happened to us in a more mature perspective, and also to see some things from my point of view. I am not sure he was able to see it that way before. Jason is a grown man now, no longer the adolescent boy he was when L. C. first came into our lives. He told me the other day that, in his heart of hearts, he knows I would never intentionally have brought someone into our lives that would hurt any of us, including his grandmother, my mother. Paula, I will never, ever get over the guilt of that. There isn't a day that passes that I don't think about Mother and my regrets, how I would change things if only I could. I miss her every single day. But I miss my son, too. I have missed him so very much!"

She paused to blow her nose.

"But now, Paula… Now Jason is willing to work on our relationship, to let me in his life again."

"That is wonderful, Kay; it truly is."

"Did I tell you what he said when I told him about L. C.'s passing?"

"No, you didn't."

"Well, you know I was very relieved; honestly, I was happy. But Jason… Well, he had a hard time dealing with the happiness of someone losing their life. He, he has a good heart."

"I'm sure he does, and I understand why he would say that. I felt much the same way."

"I just love my son so very much! All I've ever wanted was for him to be happy, to know he was loved."

I had come to know Kay well over the years. There was no question that Kay would not have done anything to hurt another person intentionally. She had no harm in her. She was not mean-spirited in any way. But she did have a broken heart. The wounds had been ripped open repeatedly throughout her life, and no doubt Jason had experienced much of the same. I prayed for continued healing for them both. Kay had long since stopped being a victim in my mind and had become a good personal friend.

Jason's wife, Katie, the same name as my own daughter's, was an incredible young woman who encouraged him to let go of his bitterness and pain, and to mend his relationship with Kay. She clearly recognized the importance of family, and she welcomed Kay back into theirs with open arms. Kay and Jason made plans to spend more time together, and for the first time since I met Kay back in January of 1994, she sounded hopeful. Hope may not guarantee a rosy future free from pain and heartache, but sometimes, just for the time being, hope is enough. To Kay, hope was everything, and it radiated from her like the first rays of sunlight after a terrible storm.

On December 1, 2019, just eight months later, Jason and Katie gave Kay an early Christmas present. Katie gave birth to Kay's first grandchild, a blonde, brown-eyed beauty they named Olivia, from the Latin word *oliva,* a term for the olive tree or olive branch, meaning… *peace.* At first sight, Olivia became the greatest source of sheer joy for Kay on this side of Heaven.

CHAPTER TWENTY-FOUR

"I can do all things through Christ which strengtheneth me." (Philippians 4:13)

"I have cancer," Kay told me on the phone only six months later.

"*What?*" I asked, incredulous. "No!"

"Yes. In both breasts. Actually, I have *two* kinds of breast cancer."

I sat down on the nearest stool in my kitchen. I did not know what to say. She was still talking, explaining, but I was having a hard time processing what she was saying. I forced myself to engage my brain.

I finally spit out, "Kay, I am so sorry to hear this!"

"I know. Only me, right?" she said, half kidding.

"What do you mean that you have *two* kinds of cancer?" I asked, realizing what she had just told me.

"I mean I have two separate types of cancer. One in my right breast, the other in my left."

"And you found out about both of them at the same time?"

"Yes."

"My goodness! I have never even heard of such a thing."

"Well, I hadn't either, but lo and behold, I have it. My doctor said, and I quote, 'it's uncommon, but not unheard of.' I was floored when I found out."

"Bless your heart! I imagine you *were* floored!"

"Yes. I was in total shock."

"Was it discovered in a mammogram?" I asked.

"Yes and no. Not until I discovered the lumps, one in each breast. They scheduled me for a mammogram, and then an ultrasound. Both tests revealed suspicious looking material around each lump."

"And you've had biopsies already?"

"Yes."

"Kay, you should have called me sooner!" I exclaimed.

"I know, I know. Everything just happened so fast."

"Kay, I don't even know what questions to ask you. I am just in shock. Two kinds of cancer...wow."

"Well, if I have to have cancer in both breasts, it is actually potentially better that they are two different types caught early, rather than one kind that spread from one breast to the other which would make it a later stage cancer." That made sense.

I marveled at her positive outlook.

Then I thought of her son and was almost afraid to ask, but I had to. "Have you told Jason?"

"Yes. He did not seem to want to talk about it with me much at first, I think mostly because he was afraid, but now he is much more supportive and communicative."

"Good, good."

"I can't tell you how much I love being a grandmother to little Olivia. She is the smartest and the cutest baby I have ever seen. Of course, I may be a bit biased, but she simply amazes me. Paula, I am determined to watch her grow up. I am going to beat this disease."

I should have been the one comforting and encouraging Kay, but here she was, assuring *me* that she was going to be a survivor of this latest valley in her life.

"I believe you," I said and prayed it would be true. "And the biopsies..."

"Well, I was referred to a surgical oncologist who performed the biopsies. I really like my oncologist, by the way. But the biopsies showed *invasive ductal carcinoma* in both breasts. You know, I never experienced any of the usual symptoms and signs of breast cancer," she added.

"What sort of symptoms?" I asked, curious.

"Like tenderness or pain at the tumor sites, or discharge, that kind of thing."

"Oh," I said. I knew frighteningly little about breast cancer.

"I did not even realize there was a lump on either side for the longest time. The only thing that bothered me was that my underwire bras seemed to irritate me. It took me a while to realize that what my bra was rubbing was actually a lump."

"Wow."

"Yeah."

"What's the immediate treatment plan?" I asked.

"I'm scheduled to have surgery on September 9th."

"Do you know what they will do in surgery specifically?" I asked. I was probably violating Kay's privacy, but she seemed eager to talk about it, and I was amazed at the strength of spirit she was exhibiting.

"I'm hoping they will only be lumpectomies. When they get in there where they can see more clearly, they may have to do more, but I am optimistic that a mastectomy or *two* mastectomies won't be necessary."

"I can come and help you, drive you, that kind of thing," I offered.

"Paula, I'm several hours away from you, and I have it all worked out. My friend is going to take me." Kay had already organized and planned for her care in her typical, efficient manner. I basically felt like falling apart, and she was the one exhibiting strength.

"Are you sure there isn't anything I can do for you?"

"Just pray for me."

"You know I will definitely do that! But if you need help afterward, you will let me come help you?"

"Yes, thank you."

Kay promised to keep me informed, and as soon as I put the phone down, I began praying right away for both her emotional and physical health. She had been through so very much, and now that she was finally able to enjoy life, she was assaulted by cancer. I was so thankful for that far better place to live after this life is over. I do not know how those who have no hope, no fear, no *Jesus,* can make it in this old sin-cursed world.

Kay did have her surgery as scheduled, which consisted of a lumpectomy in each breast. Mastectomies were not required, which was a direct answer to prayer. The two tumors were 3.5 and 2.2 centimeters, respectively, and each one was diagnosed as a stage two, nearly stage three cancer. Kay's treatment consisted of twenty-five rounds of radiation which she completed five days per week at a time, and chemotherapy which she takes in oral form, most likely for the rest of her life. The treatment caused her to lose some, but not all, of her hair and left her extremely tired, but otherwise in good spirits. Kay consented to my sharing her medical information in hopes that it may help someone else fighting similar battles.

Once Kay completed her radiation treatments, Kay called me with more news, and this time, the news was wonderful: Her most recent scans were clear.

"That's the best news, Kay!" I exclaimed.

"And that's not all the news I have… I sold my house!"

"You did?" I asked.

"Yes. I am moving to South Carolina!"

"You're moving near Jason and Katie!" I gathered.

"Yes! I'm purchasing a townhouse only a few minutes' drive from them. The best part is they seem just as excited about it as I am!"

"And I'm excited for all three – no – all *four* of you!" I said, counting little Olivia.

"I kind of feel like I have a second chance at life, like I'm starting over from scratch," Kay said.

"You won't be starting from scratch, though. You will be starting from experience. That is a great advantage!" I said, hoping to embolden her.

"Older and wiser, I guess?"

"Definitely."

The central focus of our conversations gradually shifted from L. C. Underwood or the terror he left in his wake. Our discussions of him became replaced by anecdotes of little Olivia's latest achievements, family and friends, the things we enjoy in retirement, and the faithfulness of the Lord. Once in a while, though, L. C. slithers in among us, unwelcome, and uninvited, causing the old fears to resurface in new and lurid forms. But he was powerless now. Insomuch as he remained in Kay's life as a bad memory, he would serve now only as a warning, a type of person to avoid in the future at all cost. No man is completely worthless, after all; he can always serve as a bad example, a really, really horrific example.

"I want to go with you on your book tour," she told me.

"Really? That would be wonderful, Kay!" I responded.

"I want to share my story with others, especially women who fall under the spell of men like L. C., and I want to teach others how to pay attention to those little red flags that pop up in a relationship, how to protect themselves and their loved ones, how to avoid making the same mistakes I made…"

"Kay, I think that is a wonderful way to turn all you have endured into something really positive!"

"I'm coming to Salisbury for a couple of days to meet some old friends. Are you available to meet for dinner?" Kay asked me. "I have some ideas I want to share with you."

"I'd love to!" I said happily. We made plans, and I looked forward to seeing her again.

When I saw her, she smiled as usual, but she seemed different somehow. I feared that she would look frail from the cancer treatments, older than her actual years. But in all the years I had known her, she had never looked more vibrant, more hopeful, in her life than she did right then! She radiated a calmness of spirit, an inner peace that I had never witnessed in her before. Her eyes, the eyes that had always reflected a heart full of sadness and fear, now shown with renewed life and vigor. At the age of sixty-nine, a bit older and a great deal wiser, Kay had proven herself to be the survivor I had always known she would be. Her strength, her determination, her sheer will to live made me proud to call her my friend. Peace, she and I had well learned, was not the absence of fear, but God's presence in it.

When someone has renewed life, you just know it. They carry it in their walk; the weight of it is light. You feel the energy of it radiating from deep in their bones, in the marrow. You feel safe in their presence, comforted, and encouraged by their optimism. It is contagious, and you desire some of the same for yourself, to hide in the recesses of your mind where bad memories reside. You hope that it seeps out into your own life and radiates to others around you, and some way, somehow, it does. You just know it.

"And the peace of God, which passeth all understanding, shall keep your hearts and minds through Christ Jesus."
Philippians 4:7

PHOTOS

Kay Weden in one of her happier moments

Kay Weden as she told her story on the TV series
Dead of Winter episode "Cold Blue"

Kay Weden

L.C. Underwood at the time of the murder

L.C. Underwood in prison

Viktor Gunnarsson in his favorite bomber jacket

Viktor Gunnarsson in Sweden just before fleeing to the United States.

Viktor Gunnarsson in happier times

Catherine Miller, Mother of Kay Weden

Catherine Miller and daughter Kay Weden

Catherine Miller Murder Scene

Miller Residence Murder Scene

Miller Residence Murder Scene

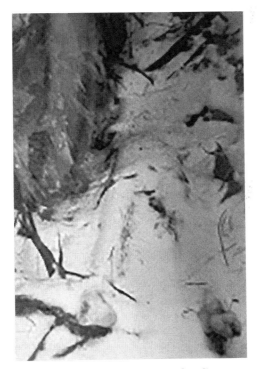

Viktor Gunnarsson Murder Scene

*L.C. Underwood in his Salisbury
Police Department Uniform*

*Watauga County Sheriff "Red" Lyons at
Residence of L.C. Underwood*

*Rowan County Sheriff's Detective Terry
Agner Digging at one of the Searches*

*Detective Sergeant Paula May revisiting
Gunnarsson Murder Scene*

Detective Sergeant Paula May in appearance on Forensic Files episode "To the Viktor"

Jason Weden, Son of Kay Weden

North Carolina SBI Agent Don Gale

NC SBI Agent Don Gale on Dead of
Winter episode "Cold Blue"

Paula May on set of Dead of Winter episode "Cold Blue"

District Attorney J. "Tom" Rusher

For More News About Paula May,
Signup For Our Newsletter:

http://wbp.bz/newsletter

Word-of-mouth is critical to an author's long-term success. If you appreciated this book please leave a review on the Amazon sales page:

http://wbp.bz/ragingona

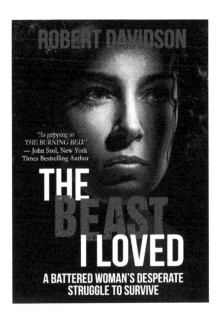

Made in the USA
Columbia, SC
03 January 2023

75443648R00170